ALSO BY *Williams Haynes*

THIS CHEMICAL AGE

The Miracle of Man-Made Materials

BY *Williams Haynes* AND
Ernst A. Hauser

RATIONED RUBBER

What to Do about It

These are Borzoi Books, published by
ALFRED A. KNOPF

THE CHEMICAL FRONT

THE
CHEMICAL
FRONT

BY
WILLIAMS HAYNES

ALFRED · A · KNOPF
NEW YORK · 1943

Copyright 1943 by Alfred A. Knopf, Inc.

Manufactured in the United States of America

Published simultaneously in Canada by The Ryerson Press

FIRST EDITION

This book has been produced in full compliance with all government regulations for the conservation of paper, metal, and other essential materials.

To an Old Friend
and Wise Counselor

WILLIAM M. GROSVENOR

WARNING TO THE READER

◇◇◇

AVOWEDLY this book contains nothing that can "give comfort to the enemy." On the contrary, it is full of facts that will cause him positive discomfort. The straightforward record of our chemical war effort cannot make cheerful reading in the Axis countries. The good news of our victories on the chemical front should, on the other hand, encourage those among us who still cherish the carefully propagandized idea that the Germans have a monopoly on all the good chemical brains in the world.

This is not a technical book and you do not need to know any chemistry to read it with understanding and, I hope, enjoyment. But you will be disappointed if you expect to find in the following pages either lurid tales of chemical horrors or mystery stories of new secret weapons.

Naturally I am revealing no military secrets, but I have also refrained from teasing you with veiled hints of mysterious chemical weapons of utter annihilation. Just between us, such prophecies are mostly moonshine, and certainly the story of our super-explosives, our combat gases, modern incendiaries, and deceptive smokes does not need the Jules Verne touch to make them more dramatic than they actually are.

I believe you will be surprised to learn that what we

think of as an ultra-mechanized war is being fought from a chemical base. Ammunition is pretty obviously chemical, but the explosion of gasoline in an airplane motor is a chemical reaction very like the explosion of TNT that bursts a block-buster, and high-octane fuel is as much a chemical compound made by chemical means as any high explosive. The bomber could not fly in the stratosphere had chemists not learned to keep lubricants from turning to thick gunk and to prevent rubber insulation from peeling off electrical wires in that extreme, thin cold. From the first shot of vaccine in the recruit's arm to the grease paint he smears on his face before he joins the raiding-party, the American soldier is clothed, equipped, armed, kept comfortable, dry, and in good health, all thanks to many chemicals; and should he be wounded new chemicals have immeasurably increased the chances of his safe, speedy recovery. There is a great deal more than poison gas in the story of modern warfare on the chemical front.

Proverbially "the squeaky axle gets the grease," and because there have been few chemical bottlenecks and almost no critical chemical shortages we hear very little about either the troubles or the triumphs of our chemical industry's war effort. Among 1,400-odd different chemicals, each in its own way vital in waging this technological war, butadiene for synthetic rubber is a significant exception. It is really significant because it is important that we Americans understand clearly why we are caught short of so essential a raw material as rubber and how it was that the synthetic rubber program came to be so badly bungled.

War on the chemical front will not end when we win victory on the battlefields of this global conflict. We should therefore learn the hard and costly chemical lessons of this war so well that we do not quickly forget them.

Chemical materials and chemical processes — especially the man-made raw materials of chemical origin such as rayons and plastics — are the greatest contributors to our new-found ability to build an economy of abundance.

Chemical progress will surely create new industries with all their opportunities for increased employment, better goods, more conveniences, greater comfort and good health. At the same time chemistry is forcing radical changes upon old-established industries. We shall see how it has revised military tactics, and it is going to upset completely our ideas about international trade and foreign relations. Unless, for example, we get a perfectly clear conception of chemical values and the chemical meaning of national self-sufficiency we shall make hideous mistakes in our postwar planning.

In telling the thrilling story of chemicals at war I have therefore been at pains to put in the background of chemicals in peace. Accordingly, you will learn — I trust quite painlessly — a good deal about certain fascinating chemical raw materials and some of the most important chemical-making processes, and it is my hope that having enjoyed this rather exciting story you will also have acquired a clearer understanding of what chemicals are and how they are produced, where they are used and what they mean to us today — and tomorrow.

                                          WILLIAMS HAYNES

Stonecrop Farm,
Stonington, Connecticut,
May 3, 1943

CONTENTS

ILLUSTRATIONS

A vivid picture of American chemical progress since World War I is set forth on the following two pages — production and wages have climbed up; prices have been brought down. The chemicals charted have been carefully selected as important items typical of different great groups. Sulphuric acid is proverbially "the old warhorse of the chemical industry." Chlorine, important not only itself, is a coproduct with caustic soda and so reflects the growth of this key alkali. Ammonia measures the development of our airnitrogen industry, and it ought to be noted that because it was not sold in tank cars in 1914, cylinder prices are used, though today most ammonia is delivered in the larger, cheaper container at a price, not of 12¢, but 5¢. Toluene is at once a coal-tar crude and a direct war munition. Phthalic anhydride illustrates expansion through new uses: originally in dyes, later in perfumes, finally in plastics.

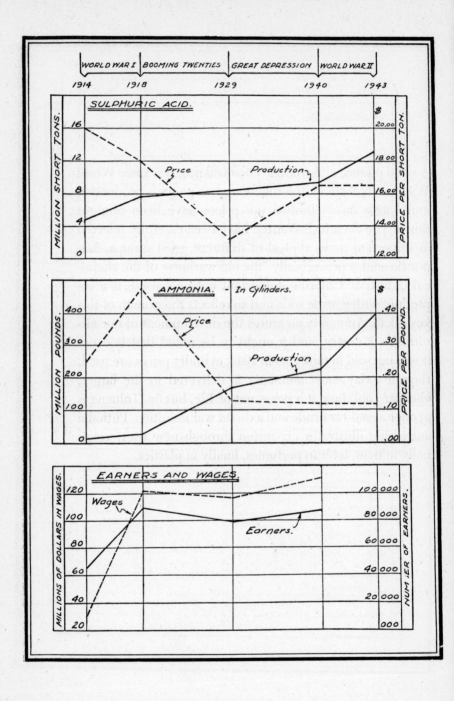

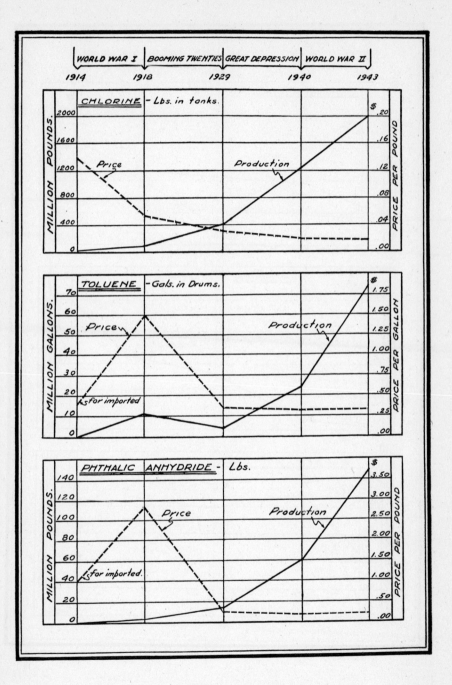

THE CHEMICAL FRONT

CHAPTER I

"AND PASS THE AMMUNITION"

◇◇◇

SEVERAL MONTHS before Pearl Harbor — it is not discreet to date this transatlantic flight too precisely — a slender, youngish man climbed into a big bomber of the Canadian ferry service at Halifax. He was carrying, very carefully, a square, 20-pound can.

That can was big hush-hush. Yet somehow or other all the crew knew that it was packed with a new super-explosive so violent that it cannot be used straight but must be diluted with TNT, so touchy that it must be kept wet. Within that 20-pound can lurked all the destructive power of an ordinary 100-pound bomb. So, very respectfully it was tucked away in the bomb bay, poised for quick dumping, if and when —

Over the Grand Bank they ran into thick fog and the pilot began making altitude. As they climbed bumpily up through the gray mist it grew colder and colder, and the crew noticed with secret amusement that their distinguished passenger was beginning to get fidgety.

This appealed to them perversely. They all knew that this passenger was the illustrious Dr. James H. Ross of McGill University, bound for the United Kingdom to teach

British munition-makers his process for manufacturing this superlative explosive. Nevertheless, he looked and talked so little like a professor of chemistry that it was strangely satisfying to have him thus revert to type. Certainly he was no absent-minded, bespectacled graybeard, this keen, sharp-featured chap with the sandy hair and the blue eyes that twinkled so friendlily. One hailed him instinctively as "Jaimie"; but here was Professor Ross twisting in his seat, tugging nervously at his earlobe. The snap and crackle of his dry Scottish wit, which had kept them all laughing, was abruptly doused as by a bucket of water. He was unmistakably apprehensive.

Suddenly he could stand it no longer. He sprang up, crawled out into the bomb bay, and brought back the can of explosive.

"This precious soup might freeze, you know," he muttered apologetically as he wrapped it up tenderly in a spare blanket.

Without another word he lay down on a bunk, tucked the can against his stomach, curled himself about it like a dog nursing his paws on a frosty night. In ten minutes he was fast asleep.

The bomber crew regarded him with open-mouthed admiration. They were accustomed to take courage for granted, but here was something different — a man who cuddled enough high explosive to blow a 50-foot crater in a city street and bash in the fronts of all the adjoining buildings! They made a grand story of it. When Jaimie Ross heard it later he laughed heartily.

"Whist, man," he chuckled, "dinna you know that so long as it's wet it's as harmless as a tin of milk?"

But Dr. Ross knows, too, that this powder, which looks for all the world like a very fine, buff-colored table salt, has when dry a detonation rate of more than 8,000 m./sec., which means in everyday language that it is downright foolhardy to stroke it with a feather.

This remarkably sensitive explosive is plainly useful in priming- and detonating-powders, and since this alert Canadian chemist learned how to make it quickly and cheaply and safely in big quantities, it is used as a charge for bombs, mines, and torpedoes. Mixed with nitroglycerin it is said to be the most powerful explosive known, too volcanic for loading explosive shells, but very handy in bombs and depth charges. Mixed in the right proportions with TNT it boosts the blast of that old stand-by by some 40 per cent. Accordingly, a bomber with fifteen block-busters so loaded packs the wallop of twenty-odd old TNT bombs. The Germans, and the Japs too, know all about this RDX, as Ross camouflaged its high-flown chemical name, for this pentaerythritol tetranitrate was discovered by a Frenchman years ago. Apparently the Axis powers do not use as much of it as they would if they knew the simple manufacturing-process Ross has worked out.

Jaimie Ross is a good working sample of how war is waged today on our chemical front. According to him his discovery of this process, so important for demolition warfare, was "only a lucky hit." True in a sense, but it is the kind of luck that blesses a Joe DiMaggio when he lines a ball between shortstop and second base, that enables a Bobby Jones to hook a brassie shot around a clump of trees onto a hidden green. Luck crowned Ross because he worked hard for years with some important ingredients of RDX and knew thoroughly their chemical characteristics and habits and how they act when brought together under given circumstances. This same brand of knowledge made easy his nonchalant but sure and safe handling of that sample can of unadulterated destruction which so dumfounded those hard-bitten airmen.

It is this chemical knowledge that makes poisonous chlorine gas out of common salt or violet scent out of stinking coal-tar, feats which appear to be as miraculous as gathering figs from thistles or making a silk purse out of a sow's ear. And it is chemical knowledge that enables us to pass the ammunition in the good old English meaning of that word, which today includes not only powder and shot, but planes and tanks, incendiaries and smoke screens, vaccines and vitamins — all the supplies and matériel of war.

We are waging technological war against technologically expert enemies. Just after Pearl Harbor we were warned of this by Watson Davis, director of Science Service. For years this cautious prophet of science has kept a keen eye on the research workers, weighing the effects of their discoveries, and when war came he forecast that the day of final victory would be determined by the speed and completeness with which those in military and economic control heeded the advice of our technically competent experts. Since then we have disagreeable proofs that he was dead right.

It is easy to forget, however, that technical war is a battle of total technology. Newspapers are filled with accounts of gigantic tanks lumbering relentlessly against the enemy, of dive bombers that swoop screaming over huddled troops, of super-submarines stalking a convoy as the timber wolves follow the caribou herd. Motorized blitzkriegs and air umbrellas cry imperatively for more jeeps and more tanks, more fighter planes and more bombers. The stupendous production of hundreds upon hundreds of thousands of these machines of war for ourselves and our allies is broadcast from every radio. "Too little, too late" has been so seared upon our war-consciousness that shortages and bottlenecks on the assembly lines have been warmly discussed at every breakfast table. No wonder we think of this as a mechanical war. Yet, in a fundamental sense of which we are not aware, it is a chemical war.

Every time a plane climbs 10,000 feet higher to a new ceiling in the stratosphere not only do its size and shape and engine have all to be redesigned, but most of its materials must also be reformulated. Five miles up rubber freezes hard as ice; insulation peels off an electrical wire like the skin of a ripe banana; metals shrink; some plastics become as fragile as a Christmas tree ornament and certain plywoods more brittle than glass; lubricating-oils turn to dough and grease is as sticky as flypaper. When a Flying Fortress in one of the first sub-stratosphere battles was hit by a burst of Nazi cannon shells, its big tailwheel tires shattered to bits like a wine glass dropped on a marble floor. Intense cold and thin air play curious tricks. Every rise of the ceiling creates new, often quite unexpected, chemical problems.

Save for chemical products — plastics, synthetic coatings and insulating-materials, artificial resins, rubber substitutes, rayon, nylon, and a host of others — not one of the vaunted machines of modern war could be built. Even their light-weight alloys are synthetic metals. The power that moves them is the mysterious, potent energy of a chemical reaction. The explosions in the cylinders of their motors differ not at all in principle from the explosion that projects the 14-inch shell from its gun. The first of all internal-combustion engines, invented by the Dutch engineer Christian Huygens in 1680, was powered by explosions of gunpowder.

It has been said bitterly that the generals are always preparing again to fight the last war. Because the American people are profoundly peace-loving, Congress has always been loath to prepare for any war. This is an expensive, dangerous combination. It is a fatal combination if a nation must face suddenly and single-handed the onslaught of modern technological warfare.

The stakes of war are high, the risks correspondingly exorbitant. Your own bridge game is less exuberant at a cent a point than at a modest tenth, and a general has many sobering responsibilities to make him conservative. Neither at the planning-board nor in the field will he take unnecessary chances, and it does not embolden him to know that while victories are loudly and generously acclaimed, defeats are swiftly, savagely punished.

Progress in war is an endless seesaw struggle between the forces of offense and the means of defense. In the first World War — at least on the Western Front — defense almost won a stalemate. Today offense is on top.

By adapting modern transport technique defense has been put to rout. The motor car has become a tank, a perfect answer to the devastating defense of a machine gun against infantry attack. The airliner, armed and armored and speeded up, simply overleaps the impregnable fortified position, the fortresses of Belgium, the Maginot Line, the citadel of Singapore. Defense has been chased out into the open. Warfare is again mobile.

This appropriation of the materials and techniques of peace is nothing new in the competition between offense and defense; but it bothers the generals no end, and that is not altogether their fault. War is not — as yet — the normal state of life on this planet, and the greatest professional soldier is in a sense a rank amateur. He has little first-hand experience and almost no opportunity to practice under actual war conditions.

It is as if a group of young physicians, fresh from medical school, were installed in an ivory tower, supplied with all the medical journals and books, given samples of the latest drugs, furnished with all the new instruments and improved apparatus, but kept for twenty years isolated from patients and clinics. Then suddenly they are put in charge of a great thousand-bed hospital in a city that has suffered an earthquake and in which a widespread fire is raging. To complete the analogy, the hospital would be manned by interns, nurses, and orderlies of whom only every fourth one is trained and competent, the other three quite inexperienced. As the stream of maimed and burned poured into the emergency rooms, we can be sure those doctors, for all their years of theoretical studies, would fall back upon the tested practices of their own first-hand experience twenty years before.

Since 1914–18 technical progress has been so rapid and

widespread that no theorist can keep pace with improved practice. In this respect the industrialist has a great advantage over the Army or Navy officers. He has the pressure of competition between new materials, new machines, new methods upon him day by day, year after year. Not only has he learned by bitter experience to rely upon the chemists, physicists, engineers, and other experts, but he has also been forced to find technical men upon whose training he can depend and whose judgment and ability he trusts.

Anyone behind the scenes of our war effort knows that those branches of our armed services are the most alert and best equipped whose daily duties are closest to the techniques of the workaday world. Thus the line officers of the Navy are modern technicians in thought, word, and deed. The Army Medical Corps, the Ordnance Department, the Chemical Warfare Service, and the Engineers, where the personnel is largely technically trained, are conspicuously up to date.

The Navy, for example, found back in 1922 that those ultra-modern materials, the synthetic plastics, could help solve a new problem. At the Harding armament limitation conference the four great naval powers agreed to build no warship of greater than 10,000 tons' gross displacement. The old battleship was out. A race was on to design the most powerful fighting ship possible within this weight limit. A pound saved anywhere in construction or equipment meant one more pound available for guns or armor plate or speed. Upon the Bureau of Ships fell this titanic task of redesign, which required a re-examination of thousands of parts, testing, comparing, and then rewriting all official specifications for the parts themselves and the materials out of which they are made.

As much as any one man can be singled out, it was J. B. Lunsford who made the Navy plastic-conscious. At a little desk piled high with papers, in a big open room of the Standards and Tests Section of the Bureau of Ships in the old Navy Department Building, he was at work rewriting all electrical specifications from the basis of 32 volts direct current to 110 volts alternating current. Throughout the electrical field plastics had already established a record of high usefulness. Plastics are lighter than metals, and this dry, New England engineer, with his typical twang and the Yankee habit of answering a question by asking another, became a plastics expert and a plastics enthusiast.

Fire at sea on an explosive-laden ship is a haunting menace not wholly banished by replacing wood with metal. A short circuit in the elaborate electrical system may start a fire that, creeping through the cables, can reach even the magazine. Shortly before, the devastating fire in New York's West Side Subway had demonstrated that this menace was no mere nightmare. But the development of the safety-flameproof electrical cable made of vinyl plastic removed this particular danger. Obviously, too, the plastic coating was lighter than the old BX cable. Furthermore, it helped the Navy to scrap its own system of 32 volts, a safety measure, and to adopt the standard 110 volts and in many cases permitted the use of regular commercial equipment.

The self-contained, long-nosed Lunsford, with his great lock of fair hair, does not impress one as a crusader. But only mention plastics — he warms up and really talks.

Probably no other man in the country knows more than he
about the properties — chemical, physical, electrical — of
so many different plastics.

Largely because of his pioneering, the Navy actually
began seeking where it might use plastics to get the most
out of the 10,000-ton limitation. Ships of the *Atlanta, Boise,
Houston* class were evolved — you recall that the *Boise*
accounted for two Japanese battleships of greater size and
heavier armament — and in them were many plastic innovations. In their wiring-systems brass outlet boxes that
weighed from three to four pounds were replaced by
molded parts weighing but four to eight ounces; gauge
cases were cut from eight pounds to one; central station
switch boards were made of laminated plastics. In the electrical system alone a saving of thousands of pounds per
ship was effected. Tons per ship were saved by replacing
the old brass speaking-tubes, another traditional safety
measure, by the sound power telephones. This feature won
the high praise of habitually taciturn Stalin when he visited units using American telephones of this new type. And
so throughout the '30's a plastic-minded Bureau of Ships
kept step with the phenomenal development of new plastics and new plastic applications. It eagerly sought where
these synthetic materials might do a better job than fabric
or rubber, wood or metal.

Synthetic plastics are but one in a regiment of new man-
made materials that range from synthetic nitrogen for fertilizers and explosives to synthetic vanillin for cake and
candy. As the Navy proved, they are not cheap substitutes
but valuable replacements. They make possible new industries such as the radio and the airplane. They are turning

old industries topsy-turvy. Applied to war, they have enormously widened the chemical front.

During the last war many of us were astonished to find how all-important chemicals were in our daily lives. Being an inquisitive and dissatisfied animal, man had learned long, long ago that he could change materials more to his liking by chemical means. The caveman was not content to hack a sharp point on the end of a stick — a mechanical operation — but thrust it into his fire and by charring — a chemical process — toughened it. Without even a name for alcohol or tannic acid he turned fruit juices into wine and hides into leather. Ages later — less than two hundred years ago — after chemists had ferreted out the commoner elements and began to have an inkling of what happens in a chemical reaction, chemicals began to be deliberately made to change materials so that they would be more attractive, more durable, more useful.

Pure, white soda-ash, made by chemical processes from common salt and limestone, replaced pot-ash, leached out of dirty wood-ashes by hot water in big iron pots, and an abundant supply of this strong, low-cost alkali made possible cheap glass, cheap paper, cheap soap. Chemistry put a pane in every window, a newspaper on every breakfast table, a bar of soap at every kitchen sink.

Soda-ash is a pretty example of the importance and benefits of chemical tools in our everyday life. We produce 3,000,000 tons of it every year in the United States and use it to make not only glass, paper, and soap, but also cleaning-powders, water-softeners, and scores of other chemicals. We refine petroleum and process textiles with it and employ it for hundreds of lesser purposes. The greatest, cheapest alkali, it ranks with sulphuric acid, "the old war horse of chemistry," at the head of the basic industrial chemicals, the indispensable tools of all industries. For many years, since long before the first World War, the United States has produced more of these so-called heavy chemicals than England, Germany, and France added together. Today our production is greater than that of all other nations, not omitting the rapidly expanding chemical industries of Russia and Japan.

The great step from making chemical tools to making chemical materials was first made in 1828, when a lanky, horse-faced chemist, Friedrich Wöhler, made urea in a test tube, without, as he said, "the aid of the kidney of dog or man." A God-fearing scientist, he was appalled that an organic substance, product of a living animal, could thus be made from inorganic, mineral compounds. No such religious scruples troubled his contemporary, the brilliant Marcellin Berthelot, who took a sardonic delight in showing up old Mother Nature by making in his laboratory all sorts of animal and vegetable materials, vinegar, alcohol, carbolic acid, many fats and oils.

This synthesis, as Berthelot called the building of complex materials out of simpler compounds, took the chemists by storm. It was helpful in teaching a lot of intricate chemistry, but it had no industrial application until 1856, when an English college student, trying to synthesize quinine out of aniline, produced by chance an excellent dye. William Perkin's "mauve," a pretty lavender quite fast on silk, was a shade impossible to produce satisfactorily with the old natural dyes and it was an instant commercial success. It launched a thousand coal-tar dyes.

PLASTICS IN THE AIR CORPS.

France had pioneered in chemical science and England in chemical industry. Germany arrived late, but she made up for lost time by appropriating coal-tar synthesis. From the fertile hydrocarbons distilled from coal-tar, she skillfully reaped a great harvest of dyes, perfume materials, medicines, and, later, high-power explosives. Her six great coal-tar chemical companies formed a cartel which by ruthless competition established a dominating, worldwide monopoly. By 1914 it had so thoroughly reduced us to a coal-tar vassalage that, although we had a big production of coke for our steel industry, we had but a small recovery of coal-tar; and what few dyes we did manufacture were made from imported intermediates. Then came World War I.

Cut off from German dyes, medicines, and explosives, we had neither the raw materials, the equipment, nor the know-how to supply these very pressing needs. More than this, our lusty, efficient heavy chemical industry was suddenly hobbled by its dependence upon foreign sources of three most necessary raw materials. Unlike the German coal-tar chemical trust, nitrates from Chile, potash salts from Germany, camphor gum from Japan were God-given natural monopolies.

We suffered a distressing chemical famine as embarrassing as it was costly. Textile mills closed for lack of dyes. Our State Department had to beg Germany to lift her embargo and then Great Britain to loosen her blockade, so that we might get ink colors to print our postage stamps and greenbacks. Salvarsan, specific against syphilis, was doled out to hospitals at $90 an ounce. Potash, essential fertilizer ingredient, went from $22 a ton to $483.63. Hundreds of chemicals vanished from the market. Chemical bootleggers flourished.

After we entered the war, in 1917, we had chemical shortages and bottlenecks, chemical priorities and embargoes. Congressional committees investigated the chemical program, and the daddies of the Farm Bloc waxed wroth over the sufferings of their constituents for lack of fertilizers. New chemical plants and increased chemical output were front-page news. To the chemical veteran all that we hear today about tanks and planes, ships and submarines, seems a curious, ironical echo of 1914–18.

During that earlier struggle our chemists and industrialists won chemical independence for the nation. They won it independently, without bureaucratic guidance, military control, or federal subsidy. And they won it so completely that the infinitely greater chemical demands of this greater war are being met without ballyhoo or hullabaloo.

"Praise the Lord and pass the ammunition!"

I sat the other day in the severely plain office of one of America's great chemists discussing these things. George Curme speaks with authority, for he has opened up an entirely new chemical field. Here, within the past fifteen years, the Union Carbide Company has created the distinctively American industry of synthetic chemicals from petroleum and natural gas, a group of products, now made by several companies, that reached in 1941 a total of nearly 2,500,000 tons and a value of more than $535,000,000. That is a pretty tangible accomplishment.

"Whatever the Army and Navy have wanted from our chemical industry they have gotten almost as simply as turning on the faucet to draw water," was how Dr. Curme summed up the situation on the chemical front. "That isn't as picturesque as hauling the old oaken bucket out of the well," he added, "and it doesn't make as lively a radio broadcast as Jack and Jill climbing the hill; but it is a much more economical and satisfactory way of procuring water. The physicists and the engineers have been getting all the publicity because they have been caught in all the jams. But Jack, you remember," he continued, smiling cheerfully, "was chiefly famous because he fell down and broke his crown. And Jill came tumbling after!"

CHAPTER II

BLACK POWDER TO
BLOCK–BUSTER

◇◇

IN THE Niagara Club, where in the atmosphere of an old English inn you can hear the saltiest chemical yarns, they are telling the story of a big handsome Canadian who, like hundreds of his countrymen, crosses the international bridge to work in one of the Niagara Falls chemical plants. He came to his foreman the other evening and said he was going to quit.

"No, Mr. Hawkins, this job ain't all right. I want to do real war work. I'm going over to the Canadian TNT plant."

"Jim, what do you think we got that Army-Navy 'E' flag for — making lipsticks? You know we're making war stuff day and night, tons of it, just as necessary as TNT."

"Well, you see, sir, it's this way. If I'm going to be killed on a war job, I figure it's braver to be blown up than poisoned."

"Poisoned, my eye! Jim, you are a goof. Did you ever even hear of anyone who lost one day's work from being poisoned in this plant?"

No, he had not, but — And then, after much probing,

the foreman learned that Jim objected to his chemical job because his girl friend said he "smelled just like a comfort station" and his pals kidded him in terms more direct and less complimentary. So they switched him out of the para-dichlorobenzene department — among many uses this chemical is the disinfectant in the pink cakes found in the public lavatories — and another labor casualty was avoided.

Jim was trumping up an excuse, but he picked one with a popular appeal. Admittedly explosive-making is danger-ous, and many of us habitually think of chemicals in terms of the drugstore as medicines or poisons, cherishing the notion that chemical manufacturing must be a notably hazardous occupation. As a matter of fact, accidents in the entire chemical group, including explosives, are 37 per cent less than for all American industries. The dangerous chem-ical operations are well known and for this very reason are carried on under vigilant chemical and physical controls. The workers are so hedged about by protection that they are actually safer in the plants than in their own automo-biles. Nevertheless, accidents do happen.

On the morning of September 12, 1941, a terrific explo-sion rocked the hills of northern New Jersey. Without warning a sudden flash of flame and then — 16,000 pounds of smokeless powder let go.

The recovery building where this big batch was in proc-ess vanished. As an echo came a second deafening roar. A near-by building burst asunder, hurling abroad another shower of glass and masonry, spraying flames and blazing bits two hundred feet in all directions.

Fire spread like a wild herd of stampeding cattle. The stunning crash of another explosion rent the smoke; then another and still another. Within the hour a square half-mile of the famous Kenvil powder plant was a charred rubbleheap, the ruins of twenty plant buildings and laboratories. Some 50,000 pounds of smokeless powder had been destroyed. Fifty-two of the plant people were dead or dying.

The newspapers hinted pointedly at sabotage. The executives of the Hercules Powder Company, rather than hunt excuses, sought to profit by the terrible experience. If that Kenvil explosion were the work of an enemy it was indeed a well-timed act of sabotage. Sixteen months later the plant, rebuilt and redoubled, was awarded the coveted "E" pennant, and at the ceremonies Major General Charles T. Harris, Jr., confessed how crippling a blow the catastrophe had been to our defense program. Struck just on the eve of Pearl Harbor, it knocked out a third of our production capacity for smokeless powder and left us with enough on hand to munition an army of only 100,000 men. At the time the higher officers of the Army Ordnance Department and the executives of the Hercules Company knew these unpleasant facts.

By long distance Hercules headquarters in Wilmington called a contractor in New York. That afternoon men were still fighting half a dozen expiring fires when two big bulldozers were already clearing the site for rebuilding. To save time no salvage was attempted. The rubble was shoved into the explosion craters, the twisted ironwork dragged aside, the mounds of brick and concrete scraped level. The new plant rose literally out of the ashes of the old with the lessons of the harrowing tragedy well applied. It had always been assumed that smokeless powder would burn, but not detonate. That echoing explosion proved differently. Accordingly, the new plant was planned and built as if it were to be a high-explosives operation. The buildings were scattered; the construction strengthened, a longer, more costly job; but it was completed by the company in four months.

Half-way to completion came the Jap attack on Pearl Harbor, a strident call to hurry, an urgent demand to expand all explosives production. Men must be pulled off the Kenvil job — engineers and draftsmen, construction bosses, even accountants, traffic men, and buyers — and the problem of training became acute. More, bigger smokeless-powder plants must be built, and operated too; cordite must be produced for our British ally, and TNT and other high explosives must be turned out, yesterday if possible, in unbelievable quantities.

Smokeless powder was the crucial need. After all, it is smokeless that fires the rifles, the machine and tommy guns; that hurls the explosive and gas shells. Especially in view of this Kenvil disaster a quick expansion to give us a plentiful supply of this propellent powder was imperative, for it is the most basic of all ammunition.

From the Battle of Crécy to our Spanish War the sole military explosive had been gunpowder. In a dim and distant past an unknown Chinese had mixed together saltpeter (potassium nitrate), sulphur, and charcoal, and no doubt he was highly astonished to discover that this mixture exploded with a bang. His simple-minded fellow-countrymen came to esteem this dangerous black powder, since its noise and smoke were plainly a great help in frightening off evil spirits. To this laudable end they devised ingenious flares and the firecrackers. When the Tartar horde swept out of the Gobi Desert on their shaggy Mongolian ponies and almost overrode Europe, they heightened the terror of their blitzkrieg by scattering these Chinese snappers among their bewildered enemies. This primitive predecessor of the dive bomber's screaming sirens was gunpowder's military debut, for though several rivals claim the honor of firing the first gun none of them, not even the mad monk Berthold Schwarz, has a clear title.

Nowadays black powder seems pretty feeble stuff. Nevertheless, it blasted out of history the strongly entrenched combination of mitered bishop and knight in armor. It thus cleared the way for our much discussed capitalistic system: a neat commentary, in passing, upon the political and economic effects of chemical discoveries.

Gunpowder was a new, startling power that did not depend on muscles. A child might employ it; a yoke of oxen could not stop it. It was easy to make, cheap to buy, handy to transport, and terrifically efficient. Its power lay in the sudden transformation of a little bit of solid into a very great volume of gases with the evolution of heat which still further expanded the gases. A single pound of black powder produces on detonation 520 cubic feet of hot gases with enough energy to lift 958,000 pounds of matter one foot in the air.

Naturally chemists began looking into this spectacular example of chemical energy. They discovered that many materials — cotton, starch, sugar, glycerin, many gums, some vegetable oils — had wonderful explosive possibilities when combined with nitrogen, and in 1846 Christian Schönbein, who strangely was a most pacific, industrious college professor, discovered that a mixture of nitric and sulphuric acids was a good agent for nitrating cellulose to nitrocellulose, or, in other words, of turning cotton into guncotton. The next year nitroglycerin was made by the same method. Both are vastly more powerful than black powder. One pound of nitroglycerin expands to 144 cubic feet of hot gases and packs a potential energy of 2,050,000 foot-pounds.

It took time, however, to find practical ways of making these improved explosives safely and employing them effectively. That nitrating process is about as safe and steady as a cantankerous mule, and not until 1887 did Vieille, a Frenchman, produce the first usable smokeless powder by treating nitrocellulose with ether and alcohol. Fundamentally his process still holds good, therefore the familiar anesthetic and the well-known stimulant are both vital war chemicals. In fact, the explosive charge that hurls a ton of steel projectile thirty miles from the cliffs of Dover against the Nazi positions on the French coast requires in processing 59 gallons of alcohol and almost twice as much ether.

The year after Vieille bridled nitrocellulose, Alfred Nobel tamed nitroglycerin by absorbing it in fine clay. He called this dynamite. This Swedish explosives genius next joined nitrocellulose with nitroglycerin by gelatinizing them with acetone as a solvent and with petroleum jelly, or vaseline, as a stabilizer. This combination is cordite, the favorite British propellent powder. Critical British need for solvent acetone was one tight bottleneck of World War I which has been smashed in World War II.

In its early days smokeless powder was of course scarce and expensive. It was therefore introduced as a sporting powder and soon demonstrated its two big advantages over black powder: it hits harder and it is really smokeless. The first advantage is obvious enough. Since nobody likes to fight blindfolded, the second appealed strongly to the soldiers. Therefore, just as soon as the technique of its manufacture had been perfected and its quality standardized, it became the universal military propellent powder.

Echoes of the bombs dropped at Pearl Harbor had hardly died away before Colonel J. P. Harris of the Ordnance Department had completed arrangements for a big expansion of smokeless-powder production. Two gigantic new plants were to be built and operated by du Pont. Hercules, still wrestling with the rebuilding of Kenvil, was to take on the third.

"You build them according to your own specifications," was what this experienced ordnance officer said in effect to the two companies, "for you must run them and turn out the goods. What we want from you is this many pounds of smokeless a day. It must meet Army standards, of course, but how you get it we don't care."

This was wise policy, born of the Ordnance Department's years of experience. Had it been followed, instead of forcing all producers to conform to a standardized operation devised by outside experts and expediters, we should have had more rubber, more atabrine, more light metals, all more quickly. The same chemical operation is never identical in two plants. Every chemical-maker works out his own ideas and learns his own little tricks. Naturally he thinks his own know-how is best, and for him it is so.

To du Pont and Hercules making smokeless powder was no experiment, but it is a complicated, tricky chemical operation with many opportunities to apply practical experience. To produce so many more pounds per day of any explosive requires a plant that must be built, a supply of raw materials that must be assured, a staff that must be trained. And the three must dovetail perfectly.

The first step in making smokeless for our Army is still Professor Schönbein's discovery that cotton can be best nitrated by nitric acid mixed with about half again as much sulphuric acid, which stimulates the reaction and maintains a high concentration of the nitric acid. A rough and ready recipe for 100 pounds of nitrocellulose is 70 pounds of well-cleaned cotton linters (the fuzz that sticks to the cottonseed hulls when the long-staple fibers are pulled off in the ginning-machines), 100 pounds of nitric acid, and 60 pounds of sulphuric acid.

The nitrocotton thus prepared — a white, pulpy mass — is washed to remove the excess acids. After wringing out, the purified nitrocotton still contains some 30 per cent water, and as it would be courting a fine blow-up to dry this by heat, the water is displaced by forcing 125 pounds of anhydrous alcohol through every 100 pounds of material in a hydraulic press. This dehydration process leaves the nitrated pulp in the form of a square block soaked with alcohol.

This block is next broken up in a mixing-machine. By adding a 2-to-1 ether-alcohol solution and agitating for about an hour, it becomes a thick, soupy mass. By pressure this mass is formed into cylindrical blocks. It is now ready for the final step.

These large damp cylinders are forced through a multitude of dies, for all the world like wheat dough coming through a spaghetti machine, and as it extrudes the nitro-cotton is cut off in short lengths. For rifle powder the dies form very small hollow tubes. For American cannon powder much larger tubes are produced with seven holes through them, one in the center, six surrounding it. Smokeless powder is thus formed into hollow cylinders of various sizes, depending upon the weapon from which it is to be fired, in order to obtain the largest possible burning surface. This helps for fast, even combustion, which results in a sudden, powerful explosion. After the grains have been formed, the green powder is carefully and very gradually dried and the ether-alcohol solvent recovered.

Since making smokeless powder is a batch operation, factories are laid out in so-called "lines" designed to handle a single lot of material continuously from nitration to solvent recovery. Each line is therefore a repetition of the same operations, and in the tremendous expansion of the past two years the munition-makers have solved their personnel problem by erecting the buildings first and by bringing their production lines into operation successively as men could be trained for each step. It is their proud record that not a single line has been held up for lack of skilled operators and also that all the plants have turned out more smokeless than their designed capacity.

Even this sketchy description of the smokeless-powder operation indicates the raw-material problems involved. Timing is as important as in a golf swing or a dance step, for as each line is brought in, the materials for it must be ready. Moreover, the demand for these materials is big and insistent. There is some recovery of excess acids and solvents. For example, of the 40 tons of ether-alcohol solvent required to produce 50 tons of powder some 25 tons are recovered for reuse.

The cotton, however, is irrevocably consumed. To make 3,000,000 pounds of smokeless a day — our present output — takes 2,000,000 pounds of cotton linters. For a year that figures out pretty close to 1,500,000 bales of 500 pounds each, or a little more than all the bales of linters we usually produce. For the duration, therefore, we have minus bales of cotton linters for rayons, moving-picture film, transparent wrapping-papers, cellulose lacquers, and some exceedingly useful plastics. The chemists have broken that bottleneck in the same way that they ducked the high, pegged price of cotton. They substitute cellulose from woodpulp for cellulose from linters.

The raw-material needs for cordite, the smokeless powder used by our British allies, are somewhat different. Cordite is a so-called "double-base" smokeless, a combination of approximately two-thirds nitrocellulose and one-third nitroglycerin, in which the solvent is not the ether-alcohol mixture, but acetone. The vigorous and most necessary "save your kitchen fats" campaign is to secure more glycerin for cordite and dynamite used in depth charges and for demolition operations. Today we hear nothing about the acetone, but during the earlier World War this was one of the most critical of all chemical shortages.

World War I caught us woefully unprepared all along the chemical front. We then had no means of supplying imperative needs for coal-tar products. Furthermore, all war chemical demands ran far, far beyond the estimates of even the shrewd German General Staff, and we were short of many familiar chemicals because existing raw materials, or the current chemical processes, or available plant equipment fell down.

Acetone became one of these critical materials. The British Army and Navy must have 50,000,000 pounds as a solvent for cordite, and 50,000,000 was just about three times as many pounds of acetone as the whole world produced. "Must have" did not mean "maybe." The British Navy had lost three good ships because shells aimed for 5,000 yards dropped innocently into the sea half-way to Admiral von Spee's cruisers. Makeshift solvents used in producing cordite failed the crucial test. In Flanders the Army was hanging on to trenches by pure grit and cold steel. The shortage of ammunition was desperate.

Frantically the British hunted every drop of acetic acid, the chemical source of acetone. Furiously they experimented with both obsolete and yet untried methods of making this water-white acid with the vinegarish odor. From these frenzied efforts sprang two new peacetime chemical industries.

Today there is no shortage of either acetic acid or acetone. More than this, these chemical industries, born of the last war, created the modern lacquers, safety motion-picture film, the safety glass of our windshields, that safe electrical cable coating the Navy adopted so effectively, the transparent plastic that makes the all-view nose and turret of our Flying Fortresses, the impregnating material of light-weight raincoats, shower curtains, and hospital sheets, and a few hundred other things from celanese rayons and vinyl plastics to improved white lead and the wonder drug sulfathiazole.

But back in 1914 one of our oldest chemical industries was the only large producer of acetic acid and acetone. As a byproduct of lumbering, thousands of cords of scrap, slabs, and trimmings were thrust into kilns and slowly burned to charcoal while from the fumes and waste liquors methanol (wood alcohol) and crude acetic acid (vinegar) were recovered. Limestone treated with acetic acid gives acetate of lime, which by distillation yields acetone.

By these simple steps some 50 pounds of acetone can be made from a cord of wood, and the yearly output of the American wood chemical industry was then about 10,250,-000 pounds. Wood must be dried six months before it can be processed, and with the high cost of the plants and the shortage of lumberjacks it was simply "not in the wood" to harvest and treat 1,000,000 cords. But there are other ways of making acetone.

First, there is the ancient fermentation process. It works spontaneously whenever cider or wine turns to vinegar: alcohol oxidizes to acetic acid. Second, there is what was then a brand-new chemical process. Calcium carbide treated with water produces acetylene — the basis of the old Prest-O-Lite lighting-systems in the primitive automobiles — and from acetylene gas acetic acid can be synthesized. Acetic acid, from either fermentation or synthesis, can be converted into acetone as in the wood process.

The good old fermentation method was worked all over the world on all sorts of materials. In India they used bamboo shoots and at Baltimore blackstrap molasses from Cuba. The Hercules Powder Company went out to the Pacific Coast, dragged ashore the giant kelp, and fermented this seaweed to get acetone so as to fill its British contract for 24,000,000 pounds of cordite. Then the kelp residue was charred and potashes leached out, thereby reviving another obsolete process and supplying another war need. The British were still short of acetone.

In the Admiralty Office somebody remembered that at the University of Manchester an odd chap, but a deucedly clever chemist, had been dabbling with some curious fermentations to get butyl alcohol in order to make butadiene to synthesize rubber. This, by the way, was twenty years before the Germans announced their now famous Buna rubber from butadiene. Somehow the Manchester professor had got a lot of acetone. Anyone with any acetone was a chance, so Dr. Chaim Weizmann was called to London. In simple terms he told a wonder tale to the hopeful naval officers.

"Ordinary yeast," he said, "turns grains, that is, starch and sugars, into ethyl alcohol and carbon dioxide which bubbles up from the fermenting mash. But other bacteria have been observed that turn these carbohydrates into other alcohols. In the beer and whisky vats they raise the devil; but I have been deliberately hunting varieties that would produce butyl alcohol, and I've found them. Unfortunately, for each two parts of butyl alcohol these bacteria make one part of acetone."

Dr. Weizmann was dumfounded when this statement of his failure was greeted with cheers. He was even more astonished to find himself and his cultures of *Clostridum acetobutylicum Weizmann* translated to the great Admiralty Laboratories working day and night to isolate a pure strain of his remarkable "alcohol bugs."

Several months later he received the greatest shock of all. He was summoned to 10 Downing Street and warmly greeted by the Prime Minister.

"You richly deserve the thanks of the nation," said Lloyd George, "and I shall be proud to recommend you to His Majesty for whatever honor you wish."

It was the turn of this humble chemist to astonish the great statesman. Weizmann refused in turn knighthood, a baronetcy, the grant of a hundred thousand guineas, and finally a liberal pension for life.

"What do you want?" cried the bewildered Lloyd George.

"I want but one thing. I have wanted it ever since I was a little boy in Russia and I am convinced it can only come from the British Government. I want a national home for my people. Promise, please, that you will use your influence to give Palestine back to the Hebrews."

Three weeks later the British Cabinet made the famous Balfour Declaration, and the rest of that story belongs to political, not chemical, history. However, Weizmann's butyl-acetone bug has had a fascinating chemical career.

The Minister of Munitions commandeered six whisky distilleries and put these bugs to work in them. As the U-boat sinkings rose, it did not make sense in England to feed grain to bacteria which could do their good work in America, close to the corn fields. So the British bought a big distillery at Terre Haute and our Government took over another at Peoria. Weizmann chaperoned his precious cultures across the Atlantic and naturalized them in the Corn Belt.

After the war these two plants were bought from the Allied War Board by a group of shrewd American businessmen. Their Commercial Solvents Company had hardly been incorporated before there occurred one of those quick somersaults in chemical demand which upset alike the old-fashioned banker, who cherishes established equities, and the new-fangled bureaucrat, who seeks security, but which both chemical technologist and industrialist welcome as fresh evidence of the swift progress that is a regular part of the chemical game.

During the war the call was all for acetone. The butyl alcohol — two pounds for one — piled up in storage tanks. Nevertheless, much research on airplane dope — the coating for the canvas wings — made from nitrocellulose or cellulose acetate dissolved in various solvents, had shown that butyl alcohol is a superior solvent for these combinations.

The Government was salvaging huge stocks of soluble cotton, accumulated for smokeless powder. Commercial Solvents had plentiful supplies of butyl alcohol.

From these cheap war-surplus materials came the first modern, quick-drying, close-clinging cellulose lacquers. They brought light, bright colors to the automobile and they broke the time jam at the end of the motor industry's famous assembly line, since they dried in as many hours as it had taken days to bake on the old varnish finishes.

But Dr. Weizmann's industrious bacteria did not fully satisfy the British needs for acetone. So English chemists turned to a synthetic acetic acid process so new it was frankly experimental. Since it started with calcium carbide, made in the electric furnace, and they had no electrical energy to spare, they came to Canada and bluntly told the officers of the Shawinigan Power Company they were elected to bring up this child of electricity and chemistry.

With a small calcium carbide plant alongside their big hydroelectrical development at Shawinigan Falls in Quebec as a starting-point they went to work. In return for use of the German synthetic acetic acid patents, which had been taken over by our Alien Property Custodian, they agreed to undertake a duplicate operation at the Keokuk Dam power-site.

Then the troubles began. Though it looked simple on paper, many kinks lurked in this new type of process. Matters were not helped much by the German patents, which, as was the German custom, omitted vital descriptions and sometimes managed to slip in misleading directions. Off in a corner of the plant two men labored over these obstacles. H. W. Matheson and H. S. Reid made a good team. The broad, husky Matheson, externally reserved but inwardly packed with high spirits, is an exceptionally competent chemist, while there are few better practical plant operators than the wiry Canadian-Scot Reid with his tiny mustache and his great heart.

When they started up the first run, Macmillan, the foreman, known affectionately as "Gas House Mack," announced dolefully: "The whole dumb show's gone dead as a corpse!"

It took a couple of weeks to learn that slight traces of phosphorus in the limestone had been carried over into the carbide and poisoned the mercury catalyst so that the acetylene reaction was killed. But eventually Canadian and American plants both got under way, and then came

the Armistice. That very day the Shawinigan Falls operation promptly blew up, whether in celebration or disgust
nobody could determine.

With the war pressure removed, the Shawinigan people
went back to first principles and at the Mellon Institute
began a thoroughgoing study of the synthetic acetic acid
process and all its ramifications and byproducts. Thus, in
answering the call for acetone, this new industry was developed in this country.

The British Army still favors cordite, the double-base
smokeless powder. Against our own single-base nitrocellulose smokeless it is a bit more powerful. It is, however, more
delicate to handle and more difficult to store, more corrosive to gun barrels, and it still requires acetone as a solvent.
Two great British-American cordite plants — Memphis operated by du Pont and Belvedere by Hercules — are sop-
ping up more acetone than was talked about in 1918, yet
there is no shortage.

CHAPTER III

CHEMISTRY REVISES TACTICS

◇◇◇

GUNCOTTON and dynamite — nitrocellulose and nitroglycerin — refined to the modern smokeless powders kicked the beam of the balance between the forces of offense and the means of defense. The equilibrium of warfare was still wabbling when yet another chemical discovery compelled all the strategists to burn up their notebooks and reports and to redraw their plans for the next war.

Smokeless powder increased both the range and the hitting-power of rifles and cannon. The battlefield, on land and at sea, had been automatically deepened. At the same time, the thick pall of acrid smoke that had curtained troops or battleships in action had suddenly vanished. Formerly gunpowder smoke had hidden them from the enemy, but contrariwise it had forced them to fire through a dense fog at unseen targets.

No longer could the army of the Duke of York, or any other commander, march up the hill and then march down again. In self-defense massed troops had to be spread out in extended order. At sea the duel between ships, climaxed by grappling irons and boarding-party, had become as obsolete as the contest between gladiators on the blood-

stained sands of the Roman arena. From both the military
and the naval points of view the battlefront had been
widened.

This was also a time of revolutionary chemical progress,
and far from the arsenals and navy yards hundreds of busy
chemists were quite unwittingly pushing forward two un-
related industrial developments which, leashed together,
were to evolve new weapons. In the steel mills chemists
were seeking tougher, more durable alloys, improved steels
more perfectly adapted for every use from the strong
bridge girder to the flexible watch-spring. In the chemical
plants they were putting together thousands of wonderful
new synthetic chemicals: beautiful dyes that were faster
to light and washing; artificial heliotrope, carnation, lily
of the valley — scents man had never been able to capture
from the flowers — scores of precious medicines; aspirin,
salol, barbital, antipyrine, salvarsan, and scores of others
to soothe and cure our ills.

Better steels made it possible to cast the big guns bigger
and still bigger, till they became too heavy for horse-drawn
artillery. Since motorized artillery was far in the future,
ordnance officers had to devise some other means of hauling the field guns out of this eclipse. They succeeded by
combining their ancient trick of cramming bullets, bolts,
and whatnot into their old muzzle-loaders with a very
modern invention, the torpedo. Thus they devised the
shrapnel explosive shell.

This new weapon demanded a new explosive possessing
highly contradictory virtues. It must be at once more stable
and more disruptive than smokeless powder. It must withstand the tremendous shock of being fired from a gun and

at the end of its flight it must shatter suddenly over the widest possible area.

The chemists were ready with the answer. In their insatiable synthesizing of new compounds they had found a number of coal-tar derivatives that can be nitrated like cellulose and glycerin to make even more powerful explosives, and some of these nitrated coal-tar chemicals proved to be the ideal shell-loading charge.

The new weapon, shellfire, had its test when the British artillery peppered the Boers with shrapnel. In the Russo-Japanese War both belligerents used explosive shells with great effect. After that the most stubborn infantryman had to admit that the rolling caissons were again something to consider seriously.

Everybody went in for high explosives and all the army headquarters began to buzz with rumors of secret weapons. The British had their lyddite; the Japs, their shimosite; the French, melinite; the Italians, pertite; and each was best of all. By 1900 any chemist interested in such matters knew that these fancy names all covered one yellow chemical, trinitrophenol, or picric acid, which had long been used as a dye and in the preparation of other coal-tar colors.

The Germans did not say much. The Kaiser's High Command and the leaders of the Dye Cartel went into a huddle, and all sorts of nitro-compounds were concocted by the chemists to be tested out by the ordnance officers. In the end they selected trinitrotoluene, TNT, as the best. This was no secret, for the United States Army had adopted the same explosive in 1904.

Then followed a military stupidity quite comparable with the diplomatic dumbness which permitted the Ger-

man nation to rearm. Admittedly these high explosives
were the acme of all ammunition. They were all coal-tar
derivatives, so that a coal-tar chemical plant was a ready-
made laboratory in which to perfect the tricky technique
of nitrating these organic compounds. Furthermore, in
event of war, it could be quickly converted into a high-
explosives factory.

The Germans wrote Q.E.D. under this proposition and
with customary completeness proceeded to force their
coal-tar chemical industry to the highest efficiency and
upon the greatest possible scale. They saw to it that no big,
self-contained rival industry developed in any other country. With fantastic stupidity the United States and British
Governments aided and abetted this plan.

Until 1885 nobody dominated the coal-tar chemical field,
and American chances in this promising department of
synthetic chemistry were then as bright as any. They were
killed by competition that, putting it mildly, was unscrupulous. One of the first tricks was plain bribery. A reasonable boss dyer might expect to find a $5 gold piece in the
top of a keg of rosaniline or malachite green. He was expected in return to specify that only these imported dyes
would enable him to give the fine shades his employers
wanted. Full-line forcing became common, German companies brazenly refusing to sell American textile mills ex-
clusive shades unless they bought all dyes from them. New
colors were introduced at fancy prices which showed such
exorbitant profits that standard, big-tonnage dyes could be
sold below the costs of American makers.

This particular malpractice was encouraged by the gen-
erosity of our own patent laws. We grant patents for new

combinations of matter; other nations allow patents only on new processes. A "product patent" prevents anyone from making new dyes or medicines even by an original method. With such a patent on acetylsalicylic acid, fortified by U.S. registration of the trade-name "Aspirin," the Bayer Company sold this popular drug here for 35 cents an ounce. Throughout the rest of the world the price was 2 cents an ounce.

All the sordid details of this brutal competition were laid before Congress at repeated tariff hearings. Its shameless exploitation of the American people was plain enough, but the chemical manufacturers and their technical experts were at pains to elucidate what coal-tar chemicals meant in peace and war and what was happening in the laboratories and plants. They got for their pains little save accusations of being incompetent and selfish, and Congress by repeatedly whittling down the tariff duties on coal-tar chemicals drove nail after nail into the coffin of what we learned with dismay in 1914 is a key industry. At the time it appeared more important to the lawmakers that "no tariff burden should be laid on the sickbed" and that the influential textile industry "should be able to buy German dyes as cheaply as possible." Both these implications of higher prices under a properly protective tariff have since been shown to have been false. American-made medicinals and dyes sell lower today than in the days of the German monopoly. The record contains no hint where, if we had no self-contained coal-tar chemical industry, the Army and Navy expected to get the new explosives in the event of war.

With the first World War came a dramatic exposé of our

chemical unpreparedness. The shortage of explosives, especially of TNT, was chronic and at times critical. Today, however, the situation is as different as white from black. Now, surplus stocks of most every type of explosive have been piled up, waiting to be loaded into shells and bombs. Possibly the greatest, certainly the least heralded, feat of our tremendous war effort has been this production of explosives to meet an enormously greater demand.

This is a bigger war, but its farflung battlelines do not alone account for its greater explosives demands. A 14-inch shell, the big shot of artillery, weighs 1,560 pounds and carries an explosive charge of 450 pounds of TNT. A 4,000-pound bomb is loaded with 2,475 pounds of super-explosives. When the RAF rains 250 tons of bombs upon a German railway center you can figure that nearly 300,000 pounds of disruptants have been loosed for their work of demolition. Bombs carry explosive charges of 55–65 per cent of their gross weight; shells, of only 25–35 per cent.

Hidden away behind these statistics are some dramatic chemical stories.

Back in 1914 toluene and phenol, the chief raw materials for the two principal high explosives, TNT (trinitrotoluene) and picric acid (trinitrophenol), came from coal-tar. Coal-tar is sweated out in the so-called byproduct of coke ovens when coal is carbonized to coke. Essentially it is similar to the destructive distillation process in which wood alcohol and crude acetic acid are collected from the fumes and liquors while hardwood is turned to charcoal. A ton of coal yields roughly 1,500 pounds of coke, 11,000 cubic feet of coal-gas, and about 10 gallons of tar. Tar is invariably a byproduct, for the ovens are operated to produce either ordinary city illuminating-gas or coke for use in converting iron to steel.

The byproducts from a coke oven are an exceedingly complicated mixture of more than 200 substances that range from gases and volatile oils through heavy oils down to solids, ending with pitch. Each component has its distinctive boiling-point. Accordingly, they can be separated in tar-refining by carefully controlled fractional distillation. Most of these components are found in such minute quantities, however, that the game of separating them out is not worth the candle. In everyday commercial practice but five are recovered, two liquids and three solids. A ton of coal thus commonly yields some 20 pounds of light oils, in which are 10 pounds of benzene and 3 pounds of toluene, and 1½ pounds of phenol (carbolic acid crystals), 6 pounds of naphthalene (moth balls), and 10 ounces of anthracene. These five are the famous coal-tar crudes.

For making high-powered explosives, therefore, precious little toluene and phenol is available per ton of coal coked. By hook and crook we managed to supply our needs for TNT during 1917–18. Today we should be hopelessly sunk had we not in the passing years developed ways of synthesizing toluene from petroleum.

At the time of the first World War a process had already been worked out by which phenol could be prepared from benzene. This process was one reason why the British had chosen picric acid as their high explosive. English chemical trade had rather specialized in disinfectants — phenol is crude carbolic acid — and their plants were better equipped to furnish the raw materials for picric acid than toluene for TNT. Working this familiar process to synthesize phenol from benzene caught Thomas A. Edison in the clutches of a German sabotage ring.

The great inventor was doing a nice business in his phonographs and he needed phenol to manufacture records. When the supply from Germany was cut off he set about to synthesize phenol from benzene and by the fall of 1914 was able to fill his own needs. The daily papers got hold of the story, for chemicals were news and Edison's was a name with which to conjure, and they played him up as the "discoverer of a great new chemical process." As he had merely adapted a well-known process he certainly did not deserve this title, but he did not disclaim it. A few months later another blast of publicity announced that Edison had contracted to buy all the light oils from the new coke ovens of the Cambria Steel Company and from the benzene produce 10,000 pounds of phenol a day. Here was a sizable surplus above his own requirements, and being no chemical merchant, Edison turned it over for sale to his friend William Hoffman, a well-known chemical jobber of Newark, New Jersey.

Down in Washington this new supply of phenol did not escape the watchful eye of Dr. Albert, commercial adviser to the German Embassy, and he began plotting to keep it out of the hands of any munition-maker who might nitrate it to picric acid for the British Army. Accordingly, arrangements had hardly been completed with Edison before Hoffman had a call from Dr. Hugo Schweitzer, the illustrious chief chemist of the American branch of the famous Bayer & Company. Safe within the private office the visitor came quickly to the point.

"I hear, Hoffman, you have the sales agency for the

Edison phenol. It ought to be very profitable. I congratulate you."

Though Schweitzer spoke with a heavy German accent, his command of English was perfect. Pausing to light a long cigar very deliberately, he assumed a confidential tone.

"Some friends of ours would like to contract for all this phenol — at a price favorable to us both."

This was noncommittal. "Friends of ours" might be friends of Germany — Hoffman was of German descent — or simply friends in the chemical fraternity. The jobber was favorably impressed and Schweitzer went on.

"The details have been carefully worked out. The phenol is to be delivered to the Heyden Chemical Works for the Chemical Exchange Association, which will be the buyer."

Hoffman looked puzzled. Heyden was, of course, the American branch of the Chemische Fabrik von Heyden, but Hoffman had never heard of the "Chemical Exchange Association" which was proposing to contract for many thousands of dollars' worth of scarce, high-priced phenol. He began a question.

"One moment, please," cut in Schweitzer. "Let me explain fully. Heyden will make salicylic acid from the phenol, a pound and a half from each pound of phenol; but they will deliver only pound for pound of salicylic acid to Chemical Exchange, which will then sell the salicylic to Bayer for conversion into acetylsalicylic acid. It's a very convenient arrangement, isn't it? Heyden gets free an average of half a pound of salicylic for each pound they make. Chemical Exchange makes a good profit on the price of salicylic against the cost of phenol. With the present demand and fancy prices for aspirin, Bayer can afford to pay almost any price for salicylic acid."

Hoffman was properly impressed. It was indeed a neat deal, a bit roundabout to be sure, but amid a chemical famine speculation was rife and double profits were quite in order. One thing worried him.

"What about this Chemical Exchange? A lot of irresponsible people are trying to break into the chemical business. I was just wondering —"

"Ah, yes." Schweitzer leaned across the desk confidentially. "You can understand that in view of my connection with Bayer it would not do for me to appear in this, so this Chemical Exchange is a little company a couple of us have organized to handle the matter. Have no fear about the money."

He drew a stout, oblong package from his pocket and quickly undid the wrappings. It contained 100 thousand-dollar bills.

"Excuse it," he said, smiling, "but we have not yet arranged our formal incorporation, so I cannot give you a check. Now I suggest that we discuss the price of phenol."

A week later Dr. Schweitzer and his dear friend Richard Kny gave a jolly little dinner party in a private room in the Hotel Astor. The guest of honor was Dr. Albert. His hosts had reason to be grateful, for he had conveniently furnished the bundle of greenbacks out of Embassy funds, and their personal profits from this deal were $816,000. Besides, they had converted a lot of phenol from potential British ammunition to harmless headache tablets. The whole nasty story came out when the Alien Property Custodian took over the two German-owned chemical companies. Dr. Schweitzer had already decamped to Mexico. The guileless Wizard of Menlo Park took a terrible ragging from his friends.

Thanks to the process of synthesizing phenol from benzene, we actually ended the war with a great surplus stock, and the twenty companies that had put up synthetic phenol plants were caught at the end of a shaky limb. They had a capacity of 100,000,000 pounds a year; the Government had a stockpile of 35,000,000 pounds; and the country's peacetime consumption was then 5,000,000 pounds. No wonder the price toboganned from $1 to 8 cents a pound or that war-built plants were scrapped right and left. To help a critical situation the Government, instead of auctioning off its surplus stocks, put this phenol in the hands of a large producer, the Monsanto Chemical Company, for orderly marketing at a fixed price of 12 cents.

Everyone was sure that phenol was stalemated for at least six or seven years. Yet within three years the immense surplus had vanished; several old war plants were being revamped; the Bakelite Corporation was building a new phenol operation of its own; the Dow Chemical Company had perfected a radically different and efficient synthetic process.

The phenol-formaldehyde plastics of the Bakelite type had found their first big industrial use. The great warehouse stocks of phenol vanished, molded into radio parts, automobile distributor-heads, and hundreds of other electrical connections and gadgets. Cheap phenol meant cheap plastics. As in the case of the cellulose lacquers made from surplus cotton and butyl alcohol, a war surplus, backed by war-won chemical experience, created a new industry, a chemical version of swords to plowshares.

The toluene story is quite different. Its supply never caught up with the TNT demand, and extraordinary efforts were made to eke out the scanty gallons sweated out in the coke ovens. To strip city illuminating-gas of the tiny fraction of toluene it contained was the quickest way, so the Army contracted with public utilities in New York and Brooklyn, Boston, New Haven, Albany, Utica, Elizabeth, Washington, Detroit, St. Louis, New Orleans, Denver, and Seattle. The good citizens of these cities "did their bit" by getting from their household gas 16 candlepower of light, instead of 18, and 6 per cent less heating-value.

The installation of thirteen additional byproduct coke operations at a cost of more than $44,000,000 was encouraged, not by the Government building these elaborate plants, but by contracting in advance to buy the toluene produced in them. Two synthetic processes to convert naphtha to toluene were tried and fizzled. But out on the Pacific Coast a tangible start was made towards the process which today saves TNT from being the greatest chemical headache of the War Production Board. What use would bombers be without bombs?

For TNT during World War I we needed 150,000,000 pounds of toluene. Somehow we managed to get it. World War II requirements are set at 3,000,000,000 pounds each year. To produce 3,000,000,000 pounds of toluene from coal-tar would mean multiplying by five our coke-oven capacity and the tons of coal coked. You might as well ask for a couple of tons of pigeon-blood rubies. We should be

SMOKE SCREEN AND PHOSPHORUS BOMB.

right up against the wicked old bottleneck of trying to get
acetone from wood that in 1914–18 so dangerously men-
aced the British cordite supplies. Acetone was not in the
wood: toluene is not in the coal.

Nevertheless, there is no shortage of TNT, thanks to an
adroit manipulation of the chemical atoms in petroleum.
Most of the many different components of both coal and
petroleum are hydrocarbons, that is, compounds that consist only of the chemical elements hydrogen and carbon. These two elements join in many mathematical combinations. But they are also put together in a number of
different patterns. Depending upon the structure of the
molecules, compounds having the same number of hydrogen and carbon atoms may differ vastly from one another
in appearance and properties, just as the letters *b a t* re-
arranged to *t a b* do not mean the same thing.

A famous group of this sort is the terpenes, hundreds of
them, all composed of 10 carbon and 16 hydrogen atoms,
or, in the chemist's shorthand, $C_{10}H_{16}$. Terpineol from turpentine, citral from lemons and oranges, and many others
from fruits, flowers, spices, and even woods and roots — all
different so-called essential oils used in perfumery and
flavoring-compounds — all are derived from terpenes. But
in each the arrangement of the 10 carbon and 16 hydrogen atoms is according to a distinct pattern, hence the different smell of oranges and turpentine.

The atoms of the hydrocarbons from coal are generally
arranged in the form of a six-sided figure, which chemists
call the benzene ring. In the lower-boiling hydrocarbons
of petroleum the atoms are strung together in long chains.
The trick is to twist the open-end chains about into the

closed-ring structure. Do this and it becomes possible to make thousands of products, now synthesized from the coal-tar crudes, out of crude petroleum.

Since coal-tar is always in limited supply, being a by-product of either the municipal gas works or the steel industry's coking-operations, this is a tempting possibility for American chemists who have vast supplies of domestic petroleum available. It is estimated by Dr. Gustav Egloff, an enthusiastic petroleum expert, that the potential supply of benzene, toluene, and xylene from the American gasoline refineries is only 85,000,000,000 pounds a year. Compared with the direct recovery of these coal-tar products in the coke ovens this is a tankcar to a teacup. To a German chemist this kind of atom-juggling is interesting but impractical. He has no spare petroleum atoms to twist into coal-tar hydrocarbons.

During the toluene famine of 1914–18 this possibility occurred to some smart petroleum technologists on the West Coast, and just as the war ended the refineries of the Central Petroleum Company and the Standard Oil of California had installed apparatus for a cracking-treatment calculated to yield 3,000,000 pounds of toluene a month. Though the new plants had cost $5,000,000 of company money, both were scrapped. But as in the case of acetic acid from carbide, they proved that it could be done. The possibilities of coal-tar products from petroleum were altogether too alluring to be dropped, and a number of oil companies continued research along these lines.

Shell, Humble, and other petroleum companies worked out independently several toluene processes, and all this technical progress has been pooled for the war effort. Into that pool have also gone the patents for the German toluene process which Standard of New Jersey acquired in its famous patent exchange contract with the German Dye Trust (I. G. Farbenindustrie), the same agreement that covers the Buna synthetic rubber patents.

Whether we need explosives or rubber more imperatively is a good deal like asking whether it is easier to live without air or water. Nevertheless, it does not appear that the American people have fared so badly in the benefits derived from this hotly disputed "patent pool." Its political aspects have been sensationally explored, but we shall find that they are not more dramatic than its chemical ramifications. At the moment, the point is that, thanks to our own American research, supplemented by German discoveries, we had ready to hand men, equipment, and the accumulated know-how so that any increased quantity of toluene for explosives has been simply a matter of expansion. When the big demolition bombs shower down on their factories and railways, Nazi chemists must kick themselves for the contribution they made to our TNT supply.

CHAPTER IV

SOME SUPER-EXPLOSIVES

◇◇◇

NITROGEN is the one essential ingredient of all explosives, and the more atoms of this element that you can tuck into an explosive molecule the more explosive it is. Nitrotoluene, with one nitrogen, is not an explosive at all; trinitrotoluene, with three nitrogens, is TNT, the most useful of the high explosives. RDX has the uncouth chemical name of pentaerythritol tetranitrate. To an erudite soul learned at once in Greek and in chemistry this tongue-twisting string of syllables suggests that "tetra" indicates four and "nitrate" is a combination of nitrogen and oxygen, NO_3. This super-explosive does, in fact, carry four nitrogens in each molecule and it is many times more powerful than TNT.

Munition-making, therefore, requires lots of nitrogen. If, as in the last war, our sole source of this explosive chemical element were the natural nitrates from Chile, we would need a fleet of more than a hundred good-sized cargo ships to bring us the equivalent nitrogen now being supplied by our synthetic ammonia plants. These capture the nitrogen from the inexhaustible quantity in the air and combine it with hydrogen in the usable form of ammonia. They guarantee us against a nitrogen famine and they re-lieve our acute shipping problem. They are simply no target at all for a prowling Nazi submarine.

A distinguished British chemist, Sir Robert Robinson, recently reminded us that the Kaiser's General Staff did not open hostilities in 1914 till Fritz Haber's process for thus wresting nitrogen from the air had made Germany munition-proof from a British blockade of nitrate imports from South America. He further suggested that the simplest way to disarm a nation is to destroy its synthetic ammonia plants.

Modern warfare depends above all else upon huge quantities of explosives and the large-scale manufacture of explosives is dependent upon the fixation of nitrogen from the atmosphere. You cannot hide an air-nitrogen plant in the cellar or throw one together like a chicken coop. Chemists cannot improvise one quickly out of a dye factory or even an alkali plant.

"If it proves expedient," said Sir Robert, "to prohibit the manufacture of explosives in Germany, Japan, and Italy, it would do a great deal to remove the perpetual menace of war, and there is certainly no nobler task before us than the firm establishment of peace." And Sir Robert quoted:

"Peace, peace is what I seek, and public calm;
Endless extinction of unhappy hates.

"If we cannot easily extinguish hate," he added eagerly, "we can do a good deal if we confine the weapons of the haters to slings, bows, and arrows."

That suggestion makes sense. Certainly chemical plants that use nitrogen can be built more easily and in less time than it takes to erect a nitrogen-fixation unit.

This colorless gas, which makes up four-fifths of the air about us, is exceptionally inert. The element that explodes so violently when combined, when free is singularly stubborn about entering into chemical reactions. Therefore it makes an ideal diluting-agent for the extraordinarily reactive oxygen that comprises the remainder of our atmosphere. Lucky for us that nitrogen is not chemically active! If it were, the metals would rust away before our eyes and we ourselves would literally burn up. However, when we wish to extract some of the 34,000 tons of nitrogen in the atmosphere above every acre of ground, this chemical stubbornness requires us to employ elaborate apparatus, great pressure, and high temperature to effect its combination.

Several methods have been discovered of capturing air nitrogen in compounds that are usable because they react readily. The most common is to combine nitrogen with hydrogen to form ammonia, NH_3. In this process pressures up to 1,000 atmospheres and temperature from 700 to 1,200 degrees Fahrenheit are employed. Reaction vessels, pumps, valves, piping, all must withstand pressures up to 15,000 pounds per square inch.

When you pour alcohol into your automobile radiator you have a simple physical mixture of two colorless liquids. The air is a similar physical mixture of colorless gases, chiefly nitrogen and oxygen. If your motor heats up to 173 degrees Fahrenheit the alcohol boils off, but the water only begins to boil at 212 degrees. To your inconvenience and expense you have unwillingly made this little demonstration of fractional distillation. Under pressure and cold the atmosphere can be liquefied, and from liquid air the nitrogen can be separated by similar fractionation.

In order to fix nitrogen gas in a compound that can be used in chemical reactions, it is mixed with pure hydrogen gas (obtained by chemical decomposition of water, H_2O) and subjected to great heat and pressure. In the presence of catalysts, which are chemicals that encourage reaction, one atom of nitrogen joins with three atoms of hydrogen to form ammonia, NH_3.

Nitric acid can be prepared from ammonia by oxidation:

$$4NH_3 \quad + \quad 5O_2 \quad = \quad 4NO \quad + \quad 6H_2O$$

ammonia   oxygen   nitric oxide   water

The nitric oxide takes up another atom of oxygen to become nitric dioxide, NO_2, and in the next reaction

$$3NO_2 \quad + \quad H_2O \quad = \quad 2HNO_3 \quad + \quad NO$$

nitric dioxide   water   nitric acid   nitric oxide

In the operation the nitric oxide formed is oxidized to nitric dioxide and gradually absorbed. The end product is nitric acid and water. And nitric acid is the nitrating-agent that turns cotton to nitrocellulose and toluene to TNT.

In 1914 there was not a single nitrogen-fixation plant in the United States, and we scrambled to build several to supplement the imports of Chilean nitrates. The original Muscle Shoals development was an abortive nitrogen plant, which after years of political bickering was turned into a hydroelectric power project with phosphate fertilizers as a sideline.

In the meantime several chemical companies carried forward the air-nitrogen experiments. The threat of Govern-

ment competition from the Muscle Shoals plant hung like
a sword of Damocles over these private developments, but
peacetime needs for this wartime necessity were growing:
more nitrogen was needed for fertilizers, for refrigeration
ammonia, for the new plastics, dyes, nitrocellulose lacquers, for many chemicals and pharmaceuticals.

The first commercial synthetic ammonia in America
came from the Niagara Falls plant of the Mathieson Alkali Works in 1923, but it was soon followed by others.
Du Pont, General Chemical and Solvay Process (units of
Allied Chemical and Dye), and Pennsylvania Salt pioneered. It was no quick and easy triumph. The du Pont
Company has confessed it took nearly $30,000,000 and a
long, lean period of twelve years before its synthetic ammonia project materialized as a profitable enterprise. Nevertheless, by the time the Japs struck at Pearl Harbor we
had a private production of synthetic nitrogen in the neighborhood of 300,000 tons, and two big Government-built
plants, operated by du Pont and Solvay, have augmented
this so that there is no shortage of this most necessary explosive element. Since every 24-foot torpedo takes 100
pounds of nitrogen and a ton TNT bomb takes 200 pounds,
this is a comfortable assurance.

Although smokeless powder, the propellant, and TNT,
the disruptant, are the backlog of military explosives, they
are not the only ones. Ammonium nitrate mixed with trinitrotoluene is the amatol of the last war. It was used almost from the first by the Germans in place of straight TNT
as a means of stretching supplies of toluene, and since it
is cheaper to make and a 50/50 mixture has virtually the
same explosive force as trinitrotoluene, it was a clever and

useful substitution which the Allies were not slow to appropriate. Amatol is smokeless, whereas TNT explodes with a sharp puff of black smoke that is helpful in range-finding, so that shells loaded with amatol are commonly fitted with smoke boxes to assist the artilleryman. Axis shells are frequently charged with this toluene-saver, for neither Germany nor Japan has any petroleum to spare for conversion from fuel to explosive, and for the same reason the British use quantities of amatol.

During the last war the Atlas Powder Company, in co-operation with British experts, built an ammonium nitrate plant at Perryville, Maryland, on the Susquehanna River, which in the record time of ninety days achieved a daily output of nearly 400,000 pounds. As part of our defense program, adopted in 1941, a much bigger ammonium nitrate plant was added to the TVA operation at Muscle Shoals.

Picric acid, which the British call lyddite, and ammonium picrate, which we christened Dunnite or explosive D, after its inventor Colonel B. W. Dunn, U.S.A., are also important shell-loading charges. Both are much used for armor-piercing explosives. The former has the disadvantage of being corrosive, so that shells loaded with it require a protective coating of tin or varnish. Dunnite, if damp, has the same fault. Both are useful because they are not easily detonated by shock or friction, which makes for safe handling.

Half a dozen other explosives and a couple of score of mixtures and combinations are used for special purposes: depth bombs, incendiaries, trench mortars, rockets, flares, and whatnot. Most of these are well known. Some are treated as secret weapons, though it is most doubtful whether there are any real secrets in explosives chemistry, that is, in the Sunday supplement sense of a new, terrifically violent explosive quite unknown to the enemy. This is true of both sides, and RDX is a good example. While it is still hush-hush in military circles, it has long been known to chemists. Much research in explosives — in plastics, fibers, coatings, and medicines too — has been stimulated by the war.

Increased use of the airplane at night has put an added value on a comparatively recent innovation in smokeless powders, the addition of certain chemicals that reduce the flash of the explosion. This flare of flame is caused by the sudden combustion of the gases ejected from the gun muzzle, and the advantage of suppressing this, especially in an anti-aircraft battery during a night attack, made it well worth while to perfect practical flame-retardants. This is accomplished by adding certain chemicals — nitroguanidine, hydrocellulose, dinitrotoluene, and several others — which by cooling the gases reduce the flash.

A couple of years before the Nazi tanks rolled into Poland, the London office of the American Cyanamid Company asked headquarters in Rockefeller Plaza: "Would you build a cyanamide plant in England?"

This inquiry came to the desk of Vice President Milton C. Whitaker, and to this shrewd, outspoken chemical executive it just did not make sense. He scribbled across the bottom: "What sort of a fishing expedition is this?" and sent it back.

Cyanamide, or more correctly calcium cyanamide, is a product of the carbide electric furnace. It was one of the earliest means of fixing nitrogen from the air. A valuable fertilizer material, it is also the starting-point in the chemical manufacture of cyanides, used in recovering metals from their ores; of acrylonitrile, which with butadiene is the base of the synthetic rubber Buna N; of guanidine, an important rubber-compounding chemical and an ingredient of one of the sulfa-drugs.

Numerous other chemical products stem from cyanamide, which the American Cyanamid Company has been for years assiduously cultivating. An interesting and useful product is cyanamide, but the British have no big, cheap surplus of electric power, hence no carbide furnaces and so but little chance of developing this chemical. Knowing this, Dr. Whitaker could find no logical reason for this inquiry.

The reply to his caustic comment was a more puzzling question. The prospective English customers, it seemed, were interested, not in a cyanamide plant, but in a carbide plant. Later it developed that what they really wanted was a plant and process to make dicyanamide. Somebody was still fishing.

The Nazi Army had not taken Warsaw before Dr. Whitaker had an important visitor from Canada, J. R. Donald, a prominent consulting chemical engineer, whose card now carried the imposing title, "Director General, Chemicals and Explosives Branch, Department of Munitions and Supply." Donald wasted no time. He looked straight at Dr. Whitaker and blurted out: "We must have 50 tons a day of nitroguanidine."

"Now, that makes some sense," — nitroguanidine makes smokeless powder flashless — "but why pick on us?"

Donald, who talks out of the corner of his mouth, shot
back the reasons. "American Cyanamid is the only maker
in North America of the basic raw material, cyanamide.
You people know more about guanidine than anyone else.
Your cyanamide plant is on the Canadian side of the Niagara Falls and uses Canadian power. You have a real
stake in Canada; Canada has a stake in the Empire; and
we need this explosive. You are tagged for the job. So I am
not asking you or advising you, I'm telling you that we
want 50 tons of nitroguanidine a day, and we want it
quick."

Whitaker chuckled. Being a straight shooter, he likes
shots that hit the bull's-eye, and he began asking questions.
Cyanamid had never made a pound of nitroguanidine and
as far as Donald knew the English had produced only a
few hundred pounds in an experimental plant. He had no
sample, but would try to get one.

"So we start from scratch, eh? At least we've made guanidine nitrate, and that's a good beginning."

"It's up to you," said Donald, grinning cheerfully, "and
we'll leave it all strictly up to you."

As a sample of how a chemical company tackles and
beats a job of that kind when left to its own initiative, that
Welland plant teaches some interesting lessons. Twoscore
experts sat down in the board room to plan the job and as-
sign the tasks. It shows also how in chemical manufacturing a complex schedule of production, calling for half a
dozen intermediate products in definite quantities, must
all be fitted together like the pieces of a jigsaw puzzle.

Starting with crude cyanamide, the major steps of the
proposed operation were visualized as first to dicyanam-

ide, thence to guanidine nitrate, so to nitroguanidine. An output of 50 tons of nitroguanidine a day would require large-tonnage production of synthetic ammonia, synthetic nitric acid, ammonium nitrate, sulphuric acid, and carbon dioxide.

Just how much of each of these basic chemicals would be required was a series of problems in chemical arithmetic which the engineers worked out: a 100-ton-a-day synthetic ammonia plant, an 80-ton nitric acid plant, a 360-ton sulphuric acid plant, and an ammonium nitrate plant with 220 tons' daily capacity. With this backlog of basic productions, it would be possible to go ahead with the main objectives, plants to produce the chemicals used directly in the preparation of the nitroguanidine.

At this point W. S. Stowell, chief engineer of Cyanamid and president of their construction subsidiary, the Chemical Construction Company, was called in. Out of their worldwide experience, building all kinds of chemical plants from Russia to Australia, they could provide working-plans for all the basic-material plants. Stowell said they could start at once on the ammonia and ammonium nitrate and the two acid plants. But the plants and processes for "dycy," for guanidine nitrate, for nitroguanidine, and for carbon dioxide from spent acid, would have to be developed and designed by the research and technical staffs of the Cyanamid Company. If these researches could be matured while the basic plants were building — well, maybe they could be out of the trenches by Christmas.

The three new chemical production jobs were now put each into the hands of committees of three qualified technologists with full authority to determine what processes

were to be used and supervise the designs for the construction of the necessary plants. Each group was charged with
full responsibility for the successful operation of the processes assigned to it. The ultimate criterion was to be a daily
output of 50 tons of nitroguanidine.

Building the new plants at Welland, Ontario, was Clark
Davis's responsibility, and this bouncing fire-ball of energy was picked by the management for this tough, rush
job with reason. He gathered together his own organization, not only construction engineers, but also chemical
engineers, chemists, and operating-men. He had the pick
of stars from the Chemical Construction staff, driven in by
the war from projects all over the globe. He borrowed
from the Cyanamid organization and he went outside for
a few outstanding men.

It was indeed an all-star aggregation which set up the
tightest of time schedules and then went to work to smash
them. Davis put up a building and then cut the windows
in its corrugated sides after the apparatus was installed.
That saved time and placed the windows just right. Materials and equipment both tightened up at the tail of the
job, but despite delivery delays the whole plant was completed in ten months.

While the new buildings were being erected in record
time a crew of Canadian technical men was recruited to
run the new operation. They were taken to Cyanamid's
Stamford Laboratories and carefully trained in every step
of the familiar and yet untried operations. When the plant
was ready they were on hand to take over actual operations.

Everyone agreed that this rather complicated combination of old and new processes in untested apparatus would require three months' tuning up. The new processes must work smoothly. All the units must be integrated. So Chemical Construction called in Carl Haner, an ace troubleshooter, to hook up. He did that ticklish co-ordinating job in three weeks.

And then they had to build a box factory. It was not a little box factory, either, but one with a capacity of 6,000 17-pound good strong boxes a day. It had been planned to pack the pale crystals of nitroguanidine for shipment to England in barrels, and everyone had been mighty proud of how cleverly an automatic flour-packing machine had been adapted to this strange task. Word came that the British wanted delivery in 17-pound boxes which could be reused for shipping TNT to their shell-loading plants.

From the first the Welland plant produced better than its planned capacity — which does not always happen in new chemical plants — and yet it cost some $2,000,000 below the estimates. To cap the climax, after final cost figures were reported American Cyanamid voluntarily sent the Canadian Government a check for $1,000,000.

"The whole Welland job," Dr. Whitaker says with forgivable pride, "was undertaken by us on a simple 'letter of intention' from the British and Canadian authorities. With that letter they placed a substantial credit at our disposal and we immediately put in motion the whole procurement program. Our construction job was well under way before the contract was finally signed. If our own Government's regular formula for doing business had been followed — well, in Washington it takes just about as long to work out a contract as it did to build the plant at Welland."

That Welland plant is also an example of the remarkable job our neighbor does in passing the ammunition. Immune from bombing and blessed with many raw materials, Canada is plainly an ideal munitions supplier. Cordite and TNT were naturally the first projects, which meant stepping up the small production at the Beloeil plant of Canadian Industries, Ltd. This meant, too, the 100-ton-a-day synthetic ammonia output at Trail, British Columbia, must be boosted by new operations at Welland and Calgary. New sulphuric and nitric acid plants were built. A little sporting powder plant at Brownsburg was expanded and now makes .303 tracer-bullet ammunition. The Canadians have built a new carbide plant to supply a new plant to make neoprene, a new nylon plant, and refineries to produce high-octane gasoline. At Sarnia they are converting butylene from refinery gases into butadiene for the production of synthetic rubber, and Dow Chemical Company is building a styrene plant. By stretching the manpower, chemical resources, and railway facilities to the uttermost, Canada actually produced more chemical munitions than Great Britain in 1942; but the shipping crisis has since forced expansion of Britain's home production.

This mighty effort has been in the hands of the Allied War Supply Corporation, which finances plant building and does all buying for Canada, the United Kingdom, and the other Allies. Chemicals are in charge of J. R. Donald, who works on the converted parking-floor of a garage in Montreal with a staff of some two dozen engineers and clerks. The whole set-up is such a contrast to our own elaborate war organizations that I blurted out in astonishment: "How on earth do you do it?"

SYNTHETICS BOUND FOR THE STRATOSPHERE.

"Oh, we just peg along," he answered. "In the early days it was tough, and we got no official help from the States. Before lease-lend your chemical people were so blasted neutral! We would not even get du Pont or Hercules to think about building us cordite or TNT plants. I don't blame them for not wanting to stick out their necks, but it made it hard for us.

"Now, everything is quite different," he continued. "We work with your Ordnance Department and the Chemical Warfare Service. Plants, patents, and practical experience are all at our disposal, and we give what we have. We're proud to have made a few interesting contributions. With our spruce and pine forests we are naturally interested in using woodpulp in place of cotton in making smokeless, and we've worked with the Brown paper people and the Hercules explosives experts in developing this important substitution. Maybe after the war it will open new opportunities in the rayon and film fields for Canadian wood industries. At any rate, it is saving us over $2,000,000 a year making smokeless, and in Canada $2,000,000 is still quite a bit of money."

CHAPTER V

SMOKE WITHOUT FIRE

◇◇

"RADIO Algiers announces" — the voice of the Washington newscaster came over crisp and clear — "that the French Desert Army, advancing on Rommel's right flank behind the Mareth Line, have occupied an important phosphate mining center south of Gafsa."

Five minutes later, John McVane, at "Allied Headquarters, somewhere in North Africa," reported another bit of chemical news from the fighting front: "The Allied Food Commission has allocated the working of the Moroccan and Tunisian phosphate mines to a British Concession."

A happy omen surely, chemical news from any of the fighting fronts being a rarity, that both these items should be heard at breakfast this very morning, March 15, 1943, as I sit down to write the story of how phosphorus has suddenly become a critical war munition and why the great North African phosphate fields are one of the high stakes in the struggle for control of the Mediterranean.

Until the Spanish curtain-raiser to the big war, phosphorus was a chemical element with but a single purpose. Many of its chemical compounds, phosphoric acid and the

64]

many phosphates, have important uses and two of them — super-phosphate fertilizer and phosphate baking-powder — run to really big tonnages. In the days before health was a matter of public concern, quantities of phosphorus went into match heads, but this strange yellow material is exceedingly poisonous and this use has long been banned by law in most countries. But in its elemental form phosphorus itself was simply and solely rat poison.

Phosphorus has uncanny characteristics. It is a soft, waxy material that cuts like a dry, crumbly cheese. In the dark it glows with a spectral greenish luminescence; in the air it ignites spontaneously, so that it must be kept under water. Mankind had found little practical use for the peculiar combination of rather weird properties of this not at all comfortable or tractable substance, that is, not until smoke became a weapon.

Yet phosphorus is vital to life. Indeed, it is an essential element in the seed of all plants and animals, and it is found in our blood, our nerves, our brains, our bones. The reputation of fish as brain food rests upon its phosphorus content, and bones were the first chemical fertilizer because they consist largely of calcium phosphate.

After Baron von Liebig proved that phosphorus, nitrogen, and potassium are the three vital elements in plant food that must be restored to the soil in fertilizers, and when Sir John Lawes discovered that bones treated with sulphuric acid yield phosphates readily assimilable by plants, bones suddenly achieved an unaccustomed commercial value. At first butcher's bones were used, but as the farmer's use of fertilizer increased, the supply proved inadequate, so they began mining the graveyards. It is said

the battlefield of Waterloo furnished the foundation of at
least two or three very respectable fortunes.

From this gruesome episode we can go straight back a
few million years to the bones of prehistoric monsters and
straight forward to the bright stream of tracer-bullets from
ack-acks that beat off last night's air raiders. The chemical
front has depth as well as breadth.

A chemical manufacturer instinctively distrusts a limited or fluctuating supply of his necessary raw materials.
That is one reason why he is not more enthusiastic about
a greater chemical use of farm crops and surpluses. The
vagaries of the weather and the pressures of group politics
do not make for a steady output or a stable price of agricultural products. By the same token, whenever possible a
chemical engineer wants to get the important chemical
elements oxygen, hydrogen, and nitrogen from air and water, carbon from coal, and calcium from limestone. These
stores are cheap, abundant, and almost universally distributed.

Aside from sentiment, therefore, the budding fertilizer
industry was not happy about this boneyard business and
it welcomed the discovery of large deposits of phosphate
rock along the coast of South Carolina. Chemically this
nubbly, crumbly material is calcium phosphate, the same
as bones, and in the Florida and North African phosphate
beds are found the fossils from the Eocene Age, underlying the teeth of giant sharks, mastodon tusks, and bone
fragments of elephants, elk, deer, horses, pigs, and other
denizens of the Pleistocene Era. These important phosphate deposits are vast fossilized prehistoric graveyards.

For twenty years Carolina phosphate rock enjoyed an

international monopoly as the source of phosphorus for plant food. It was due not a little to this big, stable, economical supply of phosphate that the manufacture of chemical fertilizers flourished amazingly. In the late '80's larger, richer beds were found in Florida and they stole the world market away from the Carolina deposits, which were beginning to peter out. Later, phosphate rock was discovered in quantities in Tennessee, but up to World War I Florida supplied most of the American, and almost all the European, demand. Its greatest use, then and now, was for treatment with sulphuric acid to produce the so-called superphosphate, essential ingredient of fertilizers.

Enormous phosphate deposits had been found in Tunisia, Algeria, and Morocco, but half a dozen small French companies, squabbling among themselves, were not a serious competitor to the American monopoly until the U-boats and the desperate Allied need for transatlantic shipping during the last war gave them a golden opportunity which they did not fumble. They established dominance over the European market and maintained it till the outbreak of the present war. Again the channels of phosphate supply have been disrupted with some new complications.

Phosphorus is a grave concern to the Nazis. Only small, low-grade deposits of phosphate rock exist in Germany, Belgium, France, and Spain. Blocked from the North African source before France fell, the Nazis drew upon Russian deposits in the Kola Peninsula till Hitler and Stalin broke their unnatural alliance. Under the Vichy regime, they had undisputed access to the North African mines. In fact, the Free French are bitter over the high-handed way in which the Germans stepped in and took over operations. They thrust an iron paddle into the seething caldron of French politics and high finance, French technology and bureaucracy, which made up the North African phosphate-mining industry.

Time and again it has been proved that when the politicians dabble in chemistry the reactions are certain to be wasteful and apt to be explosive, and yet it was fated that the North African phosphate fields should fall under the baneful sway of officialdom. In the beginning, that is, during the '20's, governmental control seemed natural and wise. Otherwise the war-born opportunity might easily have been whittled away.

North African phosphate rock is of good quality, not so rich as Florida's best, but acceptable to Continental fertilizer- and chemical-makers. The mining-companies in that field, however, were implacable rivals. Among them agreement was impossible. The American companies, thanks to the Webb-Pomerene Law under which they had organized an association to handle all their foreign sales, were able to present a united front. They also had the advantages of established, experienced sales representatives in the chief European cities, of superior mining and cleaning equipment, and of better transportation facilities for shorter hauls to their seaports. To protect the heavy French investments in the African phosphate fields, it was inevitable that the French Government should take a hand.

This step became imperative with the discovery of the Moroccan mines. These were so rich and so favorably situated for shipment from the good Atlantic ports of Safi and Casablanca that in knock-down-drag-out competition they could have put the Tunisian and Algerian mines out of

MODERN MINING EQUIPMENT.

business. And these new-found mines in Morocco were a French Government monopoly.

The independent mine owners began fighting for their lives, and most of the fighting was done in Paris. The situation was especially desperate in Tunisia, since the whole country was heavily dependent upon the activities of phosphate mining. Larger and richer Algeria, however, was a pet French colony, so patriotic and financial interests supported the shrewd Bey of Tunis in his political wire-pulling to save his own considerable private stake in phosphates. The multitude of French political parties took sides — vigorous exploitation of the Government monopoly versus the preservation of French private interests — and out of the welter came the Comptoir des Phosphates d'Algérie et de Tunisie.

The Comptoir was, and still is so far as one can learn, a compulsory, Government-backed cartel. The Office Chérifien des Phosphates, representative of the French and Moroccan Governments in the phosphate-mining business, is naturally an influential member, but the other mine owners are also in the pool. Production allotments have been arranged so that all get a reasonable share. Prior to the Vichy regime their representative and negotiator in the world phosphate trade was the capable and sincere M. de Bailliencourt, a handsome, red-cheeked gentleman of polished ability.

This Comptoir was indisputably a sensible solution of an otherwise suicidal competition that would have squandered the natural resources of this region with profit to neither the Government nor the operators. Its dealings with customers and competitors have been fair. The positive threat of American competition kept prices reasonable, and the cartel has encouraged improved mining-technique and fostered railways, docks, waterworks, and other public facilities. It even came to America for technical and engineering skill to build a great electric smelting-furnace at Pierrefitte-Nestalas in the Pyrenees. From 1927 to 1929 that ultra-American, Monsanto's vice president, Robert R. Cole, a thick-set, ruddy-faced business-man-engineer, struggled with French verbs and relished the pleasant living of the South of France, while he and his Swiss assistant, Fritz Andreae, helped Chief Engineer Seladeux of the Comptoir staff build that model plant.

External so healthy, the Comptoir suffered wasting internal diseases. Production allotments for the individual companies generated political pressures. Every investment in public utilities added to these stresses. A tumorous crop of political plums flourished. In 1932 the Governors of the three districts, the Bey of Tunis, the Mining Committee of the Chamber of Deputies, and the French Colonial Office formed a governing committee to control the mines and make allotments. This proved an effective antidote, if not a cure, to the political ills, and one of the early decrees of the Vichy Government ordered that the *status quo ante* be maintained. New quotas, influenced no doubt by Nazi compulsion, were established in October 1942.

Meanwhile how much phosphate did the Germans smuggle across the Mediterranean between the ships of the British patrols? It is a question that raises provoking questions of tactics on the chemical front, and the best authorities do not agree.

Normally North Africa shipped to Europe more than

4,000,000 tons of phosphate rock: Algeria, 600,000 tons; Morocco, 1,500,000; Tunisia, 2,000,000. How much was shipped in 1941–42 is a military secret of the Axis.

We know that both the enemy-held and neutral countries of Northern Europe get precious little. Belgium, in 1941, had about one-thirtieth of her customary supply, but Spain got her average of about 500,000 tons, and one naturally suspects some of this found its way to Germany. The hidden figures are the exports to Italy and France, for certainly these would have been available to the Nazis. Most of these must have slipped out of Bougie and Bône from the Algerian fields at M'zaita and from Sousse and Sfax from the most important mines in the Gafsa area.

We have all learned enough North African geography to recognize these once-unfamiliar names and to visualize how simple it would be to ship across to Sicily, the Italian mainland, or to the French Mediterranean ports. The two best-informed available experts that I know have quite opposite opinions.

The president of the American Phosphate Export Association, the soft-spoken, astute, very intelligent Morgan H. Grace, says: "The Germans can hardly have gotten out much more than 1,500,000 tons in 1942. As their prewar imports were nearly twice this, they cannot have much of a phosphate stockpile."

An alert French mining man, Count Henri de Lyrot, former member of the Chamber of Deputies, says: "I fear the Germans are well stocked with phosphates. How much? Possibly 3,000,000 tons. The cargo ships and planes which kept Rommel supplied during 1940–42 did not return empty. They systematically stripped North Africa of grain, vegetable oils, and phosphates; and I suspect that, from the American invasion to the taking of Gafsa in the early spring of 1942, they paid particular attention to phosphates. It would be sensible to do so, would it not?"

Sensible indeed, for, cut off from Africa, the Germans know that their supply of this war chemical is in jeopardy and that the phosphate they can recover even from their big steel industry working on the heavy phosphate-bearing iron ores will furnish but a fraction of their fertilizer and munitions needs for this element.

On the food front Germany has a vital stake in phosphates. She must buck up her overworked farmlands with phosphatic fertilizers; she also needs calcium phosphates to enrich flour as a replacement for the milk and eggs which supply the necessary calcium and phosphorus in the human diet. Then the Nazis must have phosphoric acid to clean metals and rustproof steel for tanks, planes, submarines, and other war implements. They require various phosphates for soap substitutes, water-softening compounds, and numerous needed medicinal preparations. On top of all came the new demand for the element phosphorus itself in the chemical armory of technological warfare.

Even had phosphorus been used in the first World War as it is used today, nobody could then have had an abundant supply of elemental phosphorus. Because a few pounds of phosphorus go a long way in rat poison, phosphorus was at that time made regularly by but one chemical manufacturer, Oldbury Electrochemical Company, which Frank Lidbury had started at Niagara Falls. Here elemental phosphorus was smelted out in a small electrical furnace.

One of the most vigorous, colorful enterprisers in the chemical field, Theodore Swann, barged into phosphorus. Swann is an enthusiast about chemicals, electric power, and the natural resources of Alabama, and he could sell sunlamps in the Sahara. Before the last war he sold electric power by the simple expedient of bringing whole industries into the territory of the Alabama Power Company, and he took a stiff dose of his own sales talk when he organized a company to produce ferromanganese, then wanted badly for alloying armament steels. His big battery of six electric furnaces had just been erected at Anniston when sudden peace knocked out the demand for his product. He seized upon the idea of producing high-strength phosphoric acid in his idle furnaces and he enlisted as his technician the chemist J. N. Carothers. Together they fought a good fight.

Phosphorus fumes are dangerous and difficult to handle. They chew up ordinary apparatus as a healthy pup demolishes a satin slipper. Plenty of technical troubles had to be solved, and the financial worries were constant and embarrassing. In the end Carothers, with the operating help of R. J. Hawn and the same Robert R. Cole who later helped the French, produced first 75 per cent and later 90 per cent phosphoric acid. Swann sold it all right, but the load at the bank was back-breaking, and in 1935 he sold out to the Monsanto Chemical Company.

At the same time, in near-by Nashville, the blast-furnace process was being developed by a man as forehanded as

Swann is impetuous. August Kochs, president of the Victor Chemical Works, wanted more, cheaper, purer phosphoric acid to make more high-grade phosphate specialties sold in the food and medicine fields. Meanwhile the American Agricultural Chemical Company began a phosphorus operation at Perth Amboy, New Jersey. Later, Monsanto and Victor moved into the heart of the Tennessee phosphate fields, close to the surplus TVA power, and began the recovery of elemental phosphorus. TVA followed this lead and in 1940 both private companies increased their furnaces so that they are now the two largest producers in the world.

Plainly we shall suffer no dearth of phosphorus for the ultra-modern munitions. The 35,000 tons produced in 1940 have been more than doubled.

This is enough, but it is not a superfluity, so that recently when a leak sprang in the cooling-jacket around the taphole of the biggest Monsanto furnace it was no joke. At any time such an accident is a serious matter. To shut down, cool off, make repairs, clean up, and fire up again meant a long break in operations. That would knock the production record to smithereens, and the crew was proud of that record. It had won the first "E" pennant in Tennessee. While the executives and engineers were studying the situation, up spoke Zip Burgess, big, burly master-mechanic.

"Boss," he said to the plant manager, "let's plug that lousy little hole while the old gal's running."

Now an electric furnace is a temperamental "gal," and working in the heat of Hades with the imminent threat of a deluge of white-hot slag bursting over you from the plugged tap-hole is not exactly a teaparty. Still, if the patching was skillfully and carefully done it might work, and it seemed worth the risk. A slip or the slightest mistake would turn loose the torrent, a terrible accident; but the hot, dangerous job was finished without mishap. The front line of battle is not the only place where heroic deeds are done in this war, and citations for gallantry are surely deserved by that mechanical crew, Burgess, the master-mechanic; E. W. Gephart, the foreman; C. C. Hanna, Jim Harlan, and Joe Pelican, with their four Negro tappers, Ulman Elston, Rufus Woods, Bob Hardnett, and Brooks Campbell.

Phosphorus began its military career as an incendiary, but it has come to be used now almost exclusively as a smoke, which, like fire, is an old, old weapon that has been revived. Its purpose, to screen troops or ships or cities from enemy observation, has become much more important since the introduction of the airplane for scouting and attack, but like the incendiaries it had its tryout in World War I. Phosphorus was one of the first modern smoke agents and it is still a favorite.

Both the American and British Navies began experimenting with smoke screens back in the '90's by producing a maritime version of the infamous "Pittsburgh fog." From this simple start the British came a long way to their highly sophisticated screened raid on the submarine base at Zeebrugge. Few deeds of pure derring-do performed in the first World War are more stirring than this carefully planned destruction of the Mole and blocking the harbor entrance at this powerfully guarded U-boat nest.

For two weeks before the raid British destroyers, carry-

ing generators for silicon tetrachloride smokes, patrolled
the waters off the Belgian coast, gradually edging in closer,
ever closer to Zeebrugge. The smoke screen they laid down
has not only the soft gray color of a real sea mist, but its
odor too, the salty tang of sea marshes at low tide. To the
enemy the wily device of the British appeared to be a perfectly natural phenomenon.

After their smoke curtain was sufficiently dense, one
drizzily night when the wind was right, the *Invincible*, the
Daphne, and the *Iris* slipped between the heavily fortified
jaws of the harbor up to the breakwater. They made that
landing in a pea-soup fog by dead reckoning, a neat feat
of seamanship, and their crews, storming the Mole, created such a panic inside the harbor defenses that the
blocking ships almost unmolested took their positions and
sank themselves. After an hour's commando fighting on
shore the crews of the three destroyers got back to their
ships and all escaped, well battered, but safe.

In the Battle of Jutland the German fleet used smoke
screens unavailingly in its dash for the open sea, but in this
war it has been more successful. Their two pocket battleships hid in the French harbor for months beneath a smoke
cloud that no doubt saved them from the repeated pound-
ings of the RAF. From there they scudded behind a smoke
screen through the English Channel to safety in the Baltic
naval bases.

On the other side, light British cruisers, though out-
ranged some 3,000 yards by the big guns of the *Graf Spee*,
were able to beat down this pride of the Nazi Navy by
darting swiftly in and out of a dense smoke screen, dash-
ing up to deliver their blows and disappearing before the

more powerful enemy could get their range. The Japanese saved apparently doomed ships by the use of smoke in the battles of Midway and the Coral Sea, hurrying them away to safety beneath these protective clouds.

On land smoke was first used in World War I by the British, who devised a smoke pot loaded with a villainous concoction of pitch, tallow, saltpeter, and black powder which they fired to hide exposed positions from raking gunfire. The first large-scale smoke-screened attack was made by the Canadians, September 20, 1915, when they stormed Messines Ridge after several thousand smoke shells had been loosed over the German positions from trench mortars. By the time we entered the war tactical use of smoke had become so well established that General Pershing cabled a request for several tons of yellow phosphorus to load smoke shells for the AEF.

From the point of view of the chemist a smoke screen is simply a myriad of microscopically minute particles of matter suspended in the air. It follows that the smaller and more numerous these particles, the better, more obscuring, and longer-lasting the smoke. During the last war, and since, many chemists have experimented diligently with all sorts of smoke materials and combinations. Phosphorus remains a basic material. Zinc and titanium and finely ground calcium silicide have all been used. One of the choice combinations is zinc oxide plus an incendiary.

Smoke is primarily a defense. We hear little about it, but it is being used to protect cities and airfields more commonly than one suspects. As the *ne plus ultra* in smoke camouflage, it is possible to produce smokes colored to order by vaporizing certain dyes. A "para toner," commonly used in paints, produces a nice red; chrysoidine and auramine give yellows; indigo, blue; induline, purplish tints; and a mixture of auramine and indigo, green.

Deeply secret work is going on in special smokes for defense against tanks and motorized transport vehicles. The idea is to develop materials that will either gum up the carburetor or corrode the cylinders or working metal parts. Possibly here lies the next great defensive weapon, the one that will tip the scales against the new omnipotent offense of the great mobile fortresses that have crashed the infantry lines.

CHAPTER VI

THE CURSE OF CALLINICUS

CALLINICUS, the clever Syrian who invented Greek fire about A.D. 660, displayed an uncanny foreknowledge of the scientific principles underlying the modern incendiary bomb. He mixed together pitch, sulphur, quicklime, and petroleum. The more water doused over this fiery combination, the more brightly it burns and the wider it spreads.

In a nutshell, this is the ideal incendiary material. In these days of chemical extinguishers it must come up to much more exacting specifications, but Callinicus assuredly had the right idea. His secret weapon — the formula for his Greek fire was closely guarded for nearly three centuries — enabled the Byzantine defenders of Constantinople again and again to repel the onslaughts of the Mohammedan Saracens.

"Ha!" they shouted, as they poured their burning brew down on the swarming attackers beneath the city wall. "The curse of Callinicus upon you!" It was splendid practical irony thus to give the wicked infidels a free sample of the torments of hell.

In time, however, the sons of the Prophet were able to

[79

turn the trick against their Christian enemies. They stepped up Greek fire by adding saltpeter, which made the flames hotter and more difficult still to extinguish, and they ladled it out to the Crusaders with withering effect during the siege of Jerusalem.

Both these violent combustibles were but medieval improvements of a very ancient weapon. Dread of fire, the Great Destroyer, hides within every animal. To ravage the enemy with fire and sword has been perfectly orthodox tactics since the beginning of human history. Flaming arrows, buckets of burning pitch, blazing fire-balls hurled from catapults, are the direct ancestors of that wonderfully contrived precision instrument the incendiary bomb. Fire had become an obsolete weapon after gunpowder had abolished hand-to-hand battles, but it was suddenly revived during the last war. It has become almost the distinguishing, typical weapon of this war.

The first use of fire in up-to-date warfare was an adaptation of its most primitive employment, but as bucket was followed by catapult, so direct application through flame-throwers has been superseded by long-distant delivery in bombs. During the first World War, flame-projectors were used by the Germans early in 1915. Only a few months later, in the first Zeppelin raid over London, May 31, 1915, the incendiary bomb made its formal debut into air warfare.

The ingenious flame-projectors did not prove popular with the German troops. Without being able to deliver much damage to the enemy, the vaunted *Flammenwerfer* turned out to be suicide squads. Those who were not burned to a crisp by backfires presented themselves as perfect targets. Even in streamlined asbestos uniforms of 1943 style, as clumsy as they are unsightly, soldiers can use fire effectively only against tanks. As was proved in Poland, fiery blasts can by this means be shot into slits and joints, but surer, safer defense against the lumbering fortresses are obvious.

The early incendiary bombs were also rather ineffective. Because it ignites spontaneously in the air and its flame once fairly started is comparatively difficult to extinguish, phosphorus was naturally one of the first incendiary charges selected. However, this element's heat of combustion is intense enough to ignite only the most readily combustible materials. As a filler for incendiary bombs it had a thorough testing during the recent Spanish Civil War and its limitations were set.

Some inventive Spaniard improvised an effective defense against the onrushing tanks by slipping a few lumps of yellow phosphorus into a beer bottle, filling it with gasoline or kerosene, capping it, and dropping this amateur fire grenade under the grinding treads. The Chinese adopted this idea, and during the late '30's a new, unexpected, clamorous demand suddenly appeared in the New York market for yellow phosphorus. I remember offering almost any price to American producers, and then scouring the jobbing-markets, to collect a ton, a few hundred pounds, even a couple of 110-pound cases for Generalissimo Chiang Kai-shek.

The beer-bottle bombs are useless against recent tank models, but phosphorus bombs are still most effective against flimsy Chinese and Japanese cities, and the "calling-cards" — bits of yellow phosphorus packed in cachets

of guncotton — as used by the Germans to fire fields of ripe
Russian wheat, will doubtless be used again. These tiny
firebugs are carried and dropped wet. When the moisture
evaporates several hours later, the phosphorus ignites and
fires the guncotton, which bursts into a long, hot flame. As
they weigh but an ounce, literally thousands can be scattered from a single plane, and they will start fires in crops
and forests. They would raise havoc in Tokyo or Osaka.
The true incendiary bomb, however, is made of sterner
stuff.

Combustion depends upon oxygen. One of the first experiments the schoolboy chemist makes is to thrust a glow-
ing match-stick into a tube filled with oxygen and watch
it burst into flames. When you perk up the embers in the
fireplace with bellows or the engineer gets up steam under
forced draft the same thing happens, more oxygen is available, and the temperature of the burning substance is
raised.

A gram of kerosene when burned gives off 11,000 cal-
ories. A calorie, you remember, is the amount of heat
necessary to raise a gram of water one degree on the centi-
grade thermometer. Whoever has read by the soft, pleasant light of the smelly oil lamp realizes that kerosene even
when burned slowly generates a lot of heat. Whoever has
lighted a kitchen range by pouring a little kerosene over
the wood knows that when it burns quickly it gives off a
lot more heat. Acetylene gas burns in the air with a smoky
flame that has a temperature of about 1,500 degrees F.
This is hot enough to ignite paper and wood. But if acetylene gas is mixed with oxygen, as in the oxyacetylene blow-
torch, the temperature of the flame rises enormously to

6,332 degrees F. This is hot enough for use in welding. It will melt steel. In fact, it is probably the highest temperature yet obtained by chemical means.

Upon just such simple data have the modern incendiary mixtures been developed. It was obvious first to seek out materials with a high heat of combustion — even Callinicus did that — and then to make available as much oxygen as possible in order to boost the rate of combustion.

Chemists had a wide range of materials with a high heat of combustion to choose from: the elements sulphur, phosphorus, hydrogen; the compounds benzene, kerosene, paraffin; the metals aluminum, sodium, potassium, and magnesium. They knew also many oxidizing-agents, such as the oxides, chlorates, and nitrates, that can make oxygen available in high concentrations.

It was possible to figure out a lot of theoretically desirable incendiaries, as in most chemical researches paper chemistry of this kind is commonly the first step, and then to work out practically these combinations. Obviously oxidants, supplying as they do their own oxygen, would be more valuable than materials such as phosphorus, sulphur, and petroleum, which absorb quantities of the combustible element from the surrounding air.

But chemists had ready at hand an excellent incendiary, developed long ago and widely used in peace as a welding-agent: thermite, a mixture of powdered aluminum and iron oxide. This generates a temperature of about 5,000 degrees F., sufficient to ignite metallic magnesium. And that is the basic principle of the most effective incendiary bomb, a charge of thermite in a case made of magnesium. The whole thing, load and shell, consists of high-temperature combustibles which are not easily extinguished. The thermite must itself be ignited and this is accomplished by a primer cap in the nose of the bomb which sets off a fuse that is often black powder and commonly runs through the center like the core of an apple.

Thermite's hot, quick combustion is used to ignite other materials that can be spread more widely and burn for a longer time. The metals sodium and potassium, various oils and pitches, potassium and barium nitrates, barium peroxide and perchlorate, red lead, paraffin, asphalt — the ingredients of incendiary mixtures are a veritable witches' brew. Moreover, the type of the booster charge, the use of explosive and delayed-action bombs, the construction of the bomb case for high penetration into buildings or for scattering over a wide area, add to a purposely bewildering combination of possible fire weapons.

The Germans have recently introduced the delayed-action incendiary bomb, which proved devastating until the British fire wardens learned its unexpected dangers. It is rumored that the Russians (there is little definite information about either Russian methods or matériel) have been doing great things with rockets fired from old shell cases, and that they are using phosphorus in such bombs to explode above troop concentrations. Similar rains of burning bits were used in the last war and it was found that these phosphorus sparks quickly eat through clothing and are difficult to put out. Since phosphorus burns are exceedingly painful, difficult to treat, and very slow to heal, their effect is disastrous to morale, and the weapon should be most effective in dislodging troops from trenches, foxholes, and from behind walls or buildings. Naturally the various incendiaries are all hedged about with great military secrecy, for the knowledge of what types are used is of great help in neutralizing their results.

General Ludendorff has confessed in his memoirs that a new type of incendiary bomb made of thermite and magnesium was ready to be issued to German aviation in August 1918. It appeared, however, that it would bring no direct military help to the desperate situation on the Western Front, and the High Command feared that its use against London and Paris would only bring harsher peace terms.

We know now that cities of brick and concrete are not so easily swept by fire as the Germans then expected, but this type of incendiary bomb has become a regular feature of today's air bombardment. In all-out global war the use of fire against munition dumps, fuel stocks, docks, railway centers, and enemy factories is as obvious as daylight and the plane is the ideal means of delivering this crippling destruction.

Revival of the fire weapon and the highly flammable fuels of motorized transport and airplane have conspired to increase the number of agonizing casualties from burns. But mercifully a trio of young American physicians has perfected scientific charms against the ancient curse of Callinicus.

Until a very few years ago medical men paid scant attention to burns. In ordinary practice they were not common, and the standard treatments — bicarbonate of soda and olive oil — were little better than an old wives' remedy, soothing, helpful to healing, but applied by rule of thumb without any definite knowledge of the effects of bad burning upon the human system and no definite means of combating them. Ten years ago the most conscientious doctor with a burn patient had no very satisfying treatment. To-day he has a choice of three with positively confusing combinations and modifications. Accordingly, burn casualties, formerly 60 per cent fatal, will undoubtedly be greatly lessened. Assuredly, too, increased knowledge of burns and improved technique of their treatment will come from the war-won experience.

The tragedy of the Poli Theatre fire in New Haven, in 1923, inspired Dr. Frank Underhill, professor of the Yale Medical School, to fruitful study of burns. He proved clearly, first, that burns cause a definite loss of the body fluids and that this loss results in concentration of the blood; and, second, that the fluid in the weeping or blistering of burn wounds is essentially the same as the clear fluid of the blood, the serum or so-called blood plasma. Dr. Underhill's facts did a great deal to stimulate work on the extraction and preservation of blood plasma, the basis of the blood bank, and to indicate its important relationship to cases of shock. He initiated a great deal of work that has resulted in a more understanding treatment of burn victims based upon a sounder knowledge of the nature of these wounds.

One of the first fruits of this serious investigation of burns was the testing of the old theory that burns produce toxins that attack the whole system. A young intern at Henry Ford's hospital, Dr. Edward Davidson, became convinced that these toxins were protein in character and he set about to control them at the burned area by a chemical that would combine with the proteins in the burn fluid.

After trying various acids he soon discovered that a mild solution of tannic acid precipitated the proteins into a leathery coating. Results were surprisingly successful. Not only did this protective coating induce prompter healing, but it also relieved the intense pain, and there was no doubt that the general condition of the patients improved markedly.

The third step forward was made in a study of the bacteria which flourish in the warm, moist burned area. Dr. Robert E. Aldrich turned to the familiar knowledge that certain coal-tar dyes have great bactericidal powers. He tried many and found that a dye known as gentian violet formed a protective coating over a burned surface, much as did tannic acid, and that this coating checked infection, induced healing, stopped pain. It has advantages over the acid treatment in that it can be sprayed on without cleaning the burn, a quicker and far less painful treatment. In 1937 Dr. Aldrich announced an improved aniline dye treatment, which he calls triple dye, since it is composed of a mixture of gentian violet, brilliant green, and acriflavine. Triple dye forms a thin, almost transparent coating, and is effective against almost every possible variety of attacking bacteria.

Along similar lines in the prevention of burn-wound infection has come the third recent method of treatment. Dr. K. I. Pickrell was the first to employ sulfa-drugs to burns. His original method, still not two years old, was a spray of sulfadiazine. Again results were unexpectedly successful, but the method was clumsy. It required spraying every two hours and messy wet dressings, but the success of his treatment set a score of good men experimenting with various sulfa-drugs and different methods of their application. Newest of the new is a soluble, transparent, flexible plastic, ethyl callulose, which is impregnated with sulfadiazine and used as a dressing over burned surfaces. It is distressing to dwell upon the excruciating agony of burn wounds and to know that there are many more of these painful casualties than in any previous conflict. It is a comfort, however, to realize that scientific burn treatment has made such steps forward that now we have broken the ancient curse of Callinicus.

CHAPTER VII

THE DOUBLE–EDGED WEAPON

◇◇

"WILL they use gas?"

How many times that fateful question has been asked during the past three years — asked from Moscow to Melbourne, in great cities and little hamlets; asked in stark terror; asked coolly, professionally; asked, too, in idle armchair speculation.

As the months have passed, this sharp question has been dulled, giving way first to wonder that the enemy has not used gas and then to forgetful indifference. It is no trick at all for us to shove unpleasant prospects away out of sight, out of mind.

It is a tradition, or a myth, for the word "gas" never seeps through any censorship, that gas bombs were dropped during the Battle of Britain, dropped not on London, but on small villages. It is declared, and denied, that Rommel left mustard-gas mines behind him on his retreat across Libya during the winter of 1942–43. In the modern tactics of a delaying action that would be an ideal employment of this weapon. British troops in shorts and half-sleeved shirts would be notably vulnerable to mustard-gas burns.

Before the Japanese admitted that their invasion of

China was a war at all, they were pretty free with their use of gas bombs from airplanes. Apparently the example set by the Italians in strafing the maskless, half-naked Abyssinians was a temptation not to be resisted. Since they have had a first-class war on their hands, the Japs, fearing reprisals, have used gas more discreetly.

Armchair strategists are likely to be consistently wrong in diagnosing the military situation, which is vastly more complex than they suspect, or in reading the military mind, which is far less subtle than they hope. In this question of gas, however, they undoubtedly have the correct answer.

Here is the same ticklish question posed to the Kaiser's High Command when their new thermite-magnesium bombs put in their hands an incendiary which was confidently believed capable of destroying London and Paris. However sensational such a devastating blow might be, however gratifying, it offered no direct military advantage, and they knew that unless the war could be won on the Western Front it was lost. Had the Prussian generals been sentimentalists they would have ordered their aviation out to a dramatic holocaust. Because the German General Staff was made up of hardboiled realists those new incendiary bombs were not used.

So it is with gas. The game has not been worth the candle. Furthermore, what was then the expectation that so dreadful and futile a blow would evoke iron retribution at the peace table is now certain knowledge that the use of gas, against either troops or civilians, will call forth swift retaliation in kind. Preparedness to use gas is the most effective defense against the use of gas, and all the armies are so prepared.

We should regard military poison gases realistically. The moment gas offers a direct military advantage, offsetting the risks, our enemies will not hesitate to use it and to use it ruthlessly. However, unless Hitler dominates the Nazi Army or Nipponese fanaticism overthrows native common sense, it is not likely that, even if crumbling to defeat, the Axis generals will load their bombers with gas and send them out over the countryside.

We should never forget that gas is an effective, economical weapon. Only the silliest kind of wishful thinking believes that it will be abandoned. Man has never hesitated to fight with whatever he could put his hand to that would give him even momentary advantage, and every new weapon forged has always been branded unfair. The abuse spewed at the elephants of Pyrrhus, King of Epirus, when they crashed through the invincible legions at Heraclea makes the denunciation of the poisonous chlorine loosed by the Germans at Ypres seem like a Sunday school sermon. The Romans always had a knack for invective. From the first savage who grabbed up a handy rock and hurled it at his enemy to the first artilleryman who fired a round stone through a hollow treetrunk bound with brass bands, the inventors of new weapons have always been barbarians in league with the devil. We still call the old names, but the new weapons, if good, stick. Usually they tip the scales in the seesaw between offense and defense.

It was on April 22, 1915, that the Germans loosed chlorine gas over a four-mile front, in a desperate effort, egged on by their shortage of explosive shells, to break the deadlock of the trenches. They introduced a really new principle in warfare. Till that time physical blows, delivered by hand or through missiles, had been the basis of both attack and repulse. Now blows were struck by chemical means and the opposing forces destroyed or incapacitated without physical contact.

Gas has certain obvious advantages over shell and shot. The rifle bullet's tiny track of death had been widely spread by the explosive shell, but the radius of a burst of shrapnel is quite limited and within this danger zone one of two soldiers standing side by side may be killed while the other escapes unscathed. Gas does not hit a target, it pervades the atmosphere over a chosen and controllable area within which no man escapes its effect. Such saturation is incomparably more efficient and economical hit-and-miss weapons. Moreover, the impact of missile weapons is instantaneous, but even the most volatile gas is effective several minutes and under favorable weather conditions the more persistent types will dangerously contaminate an area for days.

These are military advantages not to be forsworn. Once chemical warfare was successfully tested — the Allies knew better than the Germans how desperately close to a break-through that initial gas attack had been — it immediately established itself. During World War I, more than 3,000 substances were critically examined as possible toxic gases. Along with this frantic hunt for new and better gases went researches on all sorts of neutralizing-agents for defense against the new attack.

Chemical warfare was not exactly original with the Germans. Although they had experimented with chemical weapons since 1900 and no doubt laid some plans to use them, the same idea was entertained during our own Civil

War. We like to think that humanitarian considerations held us back. The fact is that three-quarters of a century ago neither chemical knowledge nor the technique of handling gases nor the resources of the chemical industries were sufficient to make gas an effective, controllable weapon. War on the gas sector of the chemical front impressively reveals our dependence upon technical knowledge and the ability to produce the huge supplies of chemicals needed to munition a modern army in the field.

Chlorine was the gas used by the Germans in their first gas attack. They released 168 tons from 5,750 steel cylinders (the same cylinders that are used commercially), mounted under the personal supervision of the great industrial chemist Fritz Haber. Straight chlorine, as the Germans used it, is not a good military weapon, since it is easily neutralized, but it is still a most important chemical ingredient of many combat gases.

Chlorine has been called the "Green Goddess"; not a female Mars, but a beneficent chemical deity who has bestowed upon the human race great gifts of health, beauty, and utility. Had it not been for chlorine the power looms, the great symbol of the Industrial Revolution, would have been jammed by their own output. A hundred years ago cloth was still bleached by the age-old process of spreading it out on the grass and exposing it for several months to the bleaching action of the sun's rays. This did very nicely so long as wool and flax were spun and woven into "gray goods" by hand, but when woolens and linens poured forth from the new, power-driven textile machinery the stream of "gray goods" literally flooded the land. The cloth now made in the cotton mills of a single English town, Oldham, would cover all the open fields of England, Scotland, and Wales with the old "bleaching-walks."

What promised to be a ridiculous impasse was broken by a French chemist, Count Claude Louis Berthollet, who put to practical use the well-known bleaching action of chlorine by absorbing it in water at the little chemical plant on the Quai de Javelle, Paris. This chemical bleach became known as "eau de Javelle."

James Watt, inventor of the steam engine, brought this innovation to England and turned it over to his friend Tennant, a Scotch chemical-maker. After long research, Tennant succeeded in combining chlorine and lime, to make calcium hypochlorite or bleaching-powder. This chemical gives up half its chlorine again in water. It became the base of a great industry. Tons upon tons were used to whiten cloth, paper, oils, and fats, even feathers and straw. A capital job was done in a few minutes, day or night, as well on a cloudy February afternoon as on a sunny July morning. In its day bleaching-powder was a most useful chemical tool. It saved millions of hours of time and much hard labor. It contributed a great deal to the production of better, cheaper cloth and paper.

Dumping bleaching-powder into water and sloshing cloth about in the solution was a clumsy, wasteful, messy way of getting chlorine gas for the bleaching job. Why not use chlorine direct? No reason at all, provided you could collect this active, poisonous gas, store it, ship it, and liberate it under control. The solution of these problems for industrial ends made possible the chlorine-gas attack at Ypres.

British Patent 13,755, issued to Charles Watt in 1851,

GAS MASKS AND GAS GENERATOR.

covers the passing of an electric current through a solution of common salt in water to produce caustic soda and chlorine. In this electrolytic process salt, which is sodium chloride (NaCl), consisting of sodium (Na) and chlorine (Cl), is decomposed and its elements separated. The chlorine atoms move to the positive pole, where they are liberated in the air and can be captured; the sodium reacts with the water (H_2O), combining with the oxygen (O) and one of the hydrogens (H) to form sodium hydroxide or caustic soda (NaOH). The second hydrogen atom in the water goes to the negative pole, where, like the chlorine at the opposite pole, it escapes in the air. The sodium hydroxide remains in solution and is drawn off from the cell. In his convenient shorthand of symbols the chemist writes down this simple but exceedingly important reaction as follows:

$$2NaCl = 2Na + Cl_2$$
$$2Na + 2H_2O = 2NaOH + H_2$$

An enormous electrochemical industry has arisen from that process, for caustic soda is the great industrial alkali and chlorine has found many uses besides bleaching. But ninety years ago the large quantities of cheap electrical power which make this industry possible were simply not available. Moreover, there was a well-established, different method of making caustic soda; and the chlorine and hydrogen byproducts did not count, since they had no market. Fifty years ago the picture changed.

The first electrolytic plant in America — at Rumford Falls, Maine, in 1895 — was in connection with a paper mill and the chlorine was used with lime to make bleaching-

powder. On Thanksgiving Day two years later Dr. Herbert
Dow started the second electrolytic plant. It was a big
step in his chemical exploitation of their raw material, native brine pumped from underground, out of which grew
the company that bears his name. July 4, 1895 — our alkali
pioneers fancied holidays for their openings — the Mathieson Alkali Works started a small chlorine plant at Saltville,
Virginia, but, attracted by cheap power, it soon moved to
Niagara Falls, to be followed shortly by the Hooker Electrochemical Company. After that progress was rapid.
These plants were operated for caustic soda. The chlorine
was converted with lime into bleaching-powder; the hydrogen was simply ignored. Chlorine gas was still unman-
ageable.

However, it was learned that chlorine can be liquefied
quite easily by cooling and pressure, and cylinders were
perfected to store and ship it safely. Chlorine had been
trapped and was first shipped in one-pound cylinders that
looked for all the world like the little gun fire extinguisher
we hang on the wall. Several hundred thousand cylinders
of from 10 to 20,000 pounds' capacity are now being
shipped all over the country daily. This ballooning expansion has been due chiefly to chlorine's beneficent properties, for besides being a deadly poison and powerful bleach
the Green Goddess is a potent germ-killer.

Chlorine went to work sterilizing America's water supplies. Conspicuous in the early safe-water campaign were
two Army medical officers, Colonel George A. Johnson at
the Chicago Stock Yards and especially Major Carl R.
Darnall, whose experiments at Fort Myer made sanitation
history. Then a famous lawsuit made favorable publicity

for the new chlorination method. The East Jersey Water Company was haled into court by the citizens of Jersey City, who objected to the terrible taste of the chlorinated water supplied them and who doubted that it was really safe. A distinguished company of experts was questioned and cross-questioned, piling up impressive, understandable evidence which the Chancery Court ruled to have demonstrated that chlorine actually did make water safe. After that City Fathers all over the country began scrambling onto the sanitation bandwagon.

By the time of the first World War safe yet palatable water was so practical that Wallace and Tiernan, specialists in this new field of public health, built a miniature chlorination plant, mounted it on a truck, drove it to Washington, and by demonstration proved that it did all they claimed. A number of these "Sterilabs" were delivered to the Army and some saw active service.

Nowadays nobody needs such a visual demonstration. Chlorination is the sole method of water sterilization that has official approval from every state board of health. One must be a raving chemomaniac, as a chemically crazed chemist might be called, to think all credit for having pulled typhoid deaths from 36 per 100,000 population in 1900 down to less than 3 per 100,000 in 1935 can be credited to versatile chlorine. Nevertheless, we Americans take for granted that water anywhere, in metropolis or village, is safe to drink because chlorination is the backbone of our national water-purification system. We have neither the need to boil our water nor the excuse to drink beer and wine that the rest of the human race enjoys.

This has, however, one disadvantage. Our sense of water danger has atrophied and our young men forget that swamp water on a Pacific island, a drainage ditch in North Africa, or a much-polluted European stream may be as dangerous as a strafing dive bomber. So the Army goes out in a big way for permanent water purification and sewage-disposal plants at the training-camps, and it employs many pure-water outfits for use in all the battle zones of global war.

The 1943 model of the 1918 Sterilab is the Mobile Water Purification Unit, equipped with pumps, filters, chlorination apparatus, and canvas tanks for reservoirs. Heavy steel cylinders of chlorine for the Sanitary Squads marked with red crosses are as frequently an item of army transport as the ones marked with blue and black crosses loaded with derivatives of chlorine for the Chemical Warfare Service.

Just as nearly all explosives contain nitrogen, so nearly all military gases contain chlorine. Furthermore, just as there are propellants, disruptants, and detonators, so there are different specific purposes for which gases are used. Fundamentally none of these is the death of the enemy. The term poison gas is after all but a bad name to hang this new weapon.

Hydrocyanic acid is a potent poison, one one-millionth of a person's weight being a fatal dose. Since one of its famous uses is to gas the holes of gophers, woodchucks, and other vermin, according to the layman's notion it should be the ideal poison gas. The French gave it a good tryout in the last war. They shelled the Germans with 4,160 tons of this lethal stuff, enough to kill 20,000,000,000 soldiers, or ten times the number of people on earth. From a military point of view the results were negligible.

It is interesting to trace out why this virulent poison is so ineffective for military use. The same reasons explain, too, why so few gases are suitable for combat and make clear the limitations of gas tactics.

Deadly killer, cheaply and abundantly made, safe and convenient to use, hydrocyanic acid gas fails to meet other exacting war requirements. It is not cumulative in its action. The body automatically neutralizes its effects up to one-thousandth of one grain in a gallon. It might seem simple to get such a low concentration on the battlefield, yet because hydrocyanic acid gas is extremely volatile and lighter than air it is almost impossible to do so. The difficulties are multiplied when the gas is delivered in explosive shells. Finally, a single gram of pulverized silver oxide scattered through the potash layers of a mask filter effectively bars this poisonous gas.

To be effective, then, a military gas must first of all be cheap and easy to prepare out of abundant, available materials. It should be heavier than air. If it is not too volatile, it will be more persistent in its effects over a contaminated area. One begins to see why, though thousands of possible gases have been hopefully concocted in the laboratory, but half a dozen are satisfactory weapons.

These chemical agents produce different physiological effects and are classified by military men on this basis:

Sternutators are nose and throat irritants which cause violent coughing and sneezing, followed by temporary physical disability. They are commonly irritant smokes, belonging chemically to the arsine group, and are considered harassing-agents. They cause but light casualties.

Lachrymators, tear gases, cause great temporary eye pain. Though quick-acting, effective in extremely small quantities, and quite persistent, they are of limited military value. Obviously they, too, are harassing-agents and being nonfatal are used by the police in controlling domestic disturbances. Less than 5 per cent of the tonnage of toxic gases used in the last war was of this group.

Lung injurants attack the bronchial tubes and lungs. Fluid from the blood passes into the minute sacs of the lungs so that death from these substances may be compared to drowning. Short exposure, only a few minutes, produces serious casualties, and even death, but the effect is not usually felt within an hour after exposure. These gases are either simple lung irritants derived from chlorine or toxic lung injurants made from arsenic, which has an additional systematic poisoning effect. More than 80 per cent of the fatal gas casualties of the last war were caused by agents of this group, notably by phosgene, but they are not hard to neutralize, and modern masks are effective protection against them.

Vesicants, or blistering-substances, produce inflammation and burns on any part of the body. Because of this versatility they are the most useful of all chemical agents. The famous mustard gas belongs to this family.

Throughout 1916 and early 1917 lung injurants were the chief war gases. But by July 1917 masks had been so perfected that they afforded complete protection unless troops were taken by surprise or were careless with their masks. Gas defense had stopped gas offense. Either new lung irritants, against which masks were not effective, had to be devised, or the mask must be bypassed by agents that attacked other parts of the body. Mustard gas was the answer, and this reply was delivered by shellfire.

On July 12 and 13, 1917, the Germans peppered British positions near Ypres — close to the place of the original chlorine attack — with the first mustard gas. Initially the English troops hardly noticed this new gas, but within several hours the effects became distressingly apparent, for this chemical, dichlorethyl sulphide, not only penetrates cloth and leather, but also rubber, and is highly toxic even in great dilutions. That capital authority Colonel Augustin M. Prentiss (I have drawn heavily upon his textbook *Chemicals in War* for the technical details of chemical warfare) has hailed mustard as "the king of battle gases." Pound for pound it produced eight times as many casualties as all other gases used in the first World War.

Though the Germans introduced mustard to warfare it was a well-known chemical. Theirs was the initial advantage of equipment and know-how for producing it by a process whose intermediate products are quite harmless. The Allies lacked these facilities, but the English were rescued by the ingenuity of Sir William Jackson Pope, who worked out a simpler, quicker synthesis of dichlorethyl sulphide. In America Professor Moses Gomberg of Michigan perfected the process which has since been adopted by all countries. Both Pope and Gomberg are just about the last persons on earth to dabble in poison gas. Curiously, the most nonbelligerent chemists seem destined to make big contributions of this sort, as witness two other

American chemists, the late W. Lee Lewis, discoverer of lewisite, and Roger Adams, who found adamsite, both college professors and notably frank, friendly men.

The hunt for combat gases goes on, for surprise is an ace of trumps in chemical warfare. But specifications are so exacting, the technique now so thoroughly understood, it is unlikely any Nazi secret weapons will catch us unprepared. No super-gas that can wipe out the population of New York or London and render the ruins fatally dangerous for weeks has been discovered except by the Sunday supplements. The laws of chemistry, physics, and physiology are not all so easily circumvented.

Military men insist, and insist again, that mustard is still king and that no notable improvement over what was known in 1918 has been developed. Practical and tactical considerations both taken into account, this is probably true. It is well known, however, that there are new war gases, such as the so-called French mustard and certain improved types of arsines, but gas defense has been as industrious as gas offense. Not only do modern masks afford greater protection; clothing and boots have also been rendered immune to the passage of vesicants by protective impregnating-materials. Because of the military value of surprise no section of our chemical armory is more heavily guarded.

A $7,000,000 expansion of the Chemical Warfare Service's plant, laboratory, and testing-grounds at Edgewood, Maryland, has been completed. Three new strictly gas, smoke, and incendiary plants, operated at widely separated points by the Dow, du Pont, and Monsanto companies, are working day and night. Finally, two enormous plants for activated carbon — no longer is it necessary for the Boy Scouts to go out collecting peach pits as they did in 1917 — have been built to provide the basic material for gas-mask canisters.

The Army views gas realistically. American troops are equipped to handle and to hand out this weapon, and they are well trained for both jobs. This is important, for proper training prevents the instinctive panicky fear of gas and instills confidence in the mask. In its latest models this is a complex mechanism of 83 distinct parts. It has been subjected to constant study for years, and a skeleton force at Edgewood Arsenal has long been manufacturing them for the old regular Army. Back in 1939 educational orders were placed with private firms, and when we entered the war more than 800 contracts were in force in 26 states for parts and assembled masks.

Every man in service gets thorough mask training in the presence of actual war gases. No American soldier embarks for the front without his service mask. If and when gas is cut loose by the enemy, we shall be prepared to take it, and, what is just as important, to hand it out. Rule Number One in chemical warfare tactics is that gas is the best defense against gas. It is the double-edged weapon of technological war.

CHAPTER VIII

TO CURE, NOT TO KILL

◇◇

"The army that wins the last battle is the army that has the best remnants." So said the brilliant von Moltke, cynically perhaps, but according to the tactics of his day with a good deal of truth.

Today the scheme of battle has toughened and our weapons are almost infinitely more destructive than those available to that determined, pitiless Prussian field marshal. But in our campaigns there are to be few remnants.

Among the thousands of casualties suffered in the sneak attack on Pearl Harbor, not a leg or an arm was lost because of infection. Limbs shattered by machine-gun bullets and shell fragments were amputated, but none that had been attacked by that old, deadly enemy, the streptococcus.

Of all wounded men who died in the first World War, more than 80 per cent died, not of their wounds, but from infection of the wounds, most of them by this same insidious bacterium. Colonel Leonard Colebrook, England's great medical authority on this dangerous microbe, thinks this appalling figure should be raised to 90 per cent. Cold statistics reveal that the death toll of all armies in the last

104]

war from injuries, not diseases, was close to 7,250,000. Three out of four of these men died on the battlefield. Of those who did reach the safety and comfort of the hospitals, with all their modern means of sanitation and their eager, skilled staffs, again three out of four who died were killed by the streptococcus. In the long, long battle against wound infection defense has at last matched this insidious attack. New weapons have turned the tide of the unequal combat. Pearl Harbor deserves to be remembered also for the victory of the sulfa-drugs.

President Roosevelt was not the only one who sent investigators to that blood-stained monument of Jap strategy. The Army's Surgeon General, James C. Magee, dispatched two distinguished experts, Dr. I. S. Ravdin, professor of surgery at the University of Pennsylvania, and Dr. Perrin Long, of the Johns Hopkins Medical School. Like Dr. Colebrook in England, Dr. Long in this country was one of the first sulfa-drug fighters against the deadly strep germs, and in Hawaii he saw with his own eyes similar miraculous sulfa-cures of which he had read in the reports of army doctors from Dunkirk and the Battle of Britain. Ten days after the attack he could find not a single case with a massive infection. Men who had sustained severe abdominal wounds, of all wounds the most vulnerable to the dangerous entrance of bacteria, were itching to get back into active service. In the crowded wards these expert observers found hundreds of critical wounds whose clean, rapid healing passed all their clinical experience, almost surpassed belief.

Back in Washington Drs. Ravdin and Long made a detailed report to General Magee. It bristled with the tech-

nicalities of medicine and surgery, praising warmly, criti-
cizing constructively, and it ended with a number of
definite recommendations. Several of these had to do with
sulfa-drugs, and on the basis of their suggestions the Medical Corps's supply officers sharpened their pencils and
began recalculating their requirements of these new
weapons.

While they were figuring, Major John Purington made a
tour of the American coal-tar chemical industry. He called
on all makers of the sulfa-group of compounds and checked
up also with manufacturers of essential intermediates
from which these medicinal chemicals are prepared. This
frank and businesslike young medical officer sat for hours,
closeted with production managers and vice presidents in
charge of sales, studying manufacturing schedules and
civilian demand. He tabulated all his careful notes; totaled
the needs of Army and Navy, of lease-lend, of private
practitioners and public hospitals; struck a balance against
current production. The deficit was staggering.

In 1940, the year before Pearl Harbor, about three-quarters of a million pounds of all the then-used sulfa-drugs
were made in this country. So swift is progress in this field
that during that year only experimental quantities, too insignificant to get into commercial statistics, were made of
sulfadiazine and sulfaguanidine while succinyl sulfathiazole had not even been discovered.

Three-quarters of a million pounds of any chemicals administered in doses that are measured in grains are a lot
of medicine. It is record-breaking when you remember
that it was only four years before when Cyanamid's Calco
Division, sensing the importance of sulfanilamide, had set

in motion the wheels of research and production that in
January 1937 turned out the first large-scale output of any
sulfa-drug in the United States.

The sulfa-drugs, though newcomers, are not upstarts.
Their family history traces back to the Adam of all coal-
tar dyes, Sir William Perkin's mauve. It is an amusing foot-
note to their chemical genealogy that the first dye synthesized was discovered by mischance when young Perkin
was actually trying to duplicate quinine, one of the only
two truly chemotherapeutic drugs found in nature. The
word "chemotherapy" no longer stops us, although the
idea of definite chemical cures for specific diseases is still
a new, but vastly encouraging conception. To chemists
and physicians it is an old dream, often roused by little
successes, time and again frustrated by failures, of late
splendidly revived.

The hope of finding among the coal-tar dyes specific
chemicals which would cure the ills of human flesh was
kindled by the discovery among them of many that killed
micro-organisms. During the early 1870's a medical student at the Strassburg University became so fascinated by
these prospects that he forsook medicine to become a bio-
chemist, one of the greatest in this exacting field of science and one of the greatest benefactors of suffering humanity.

One day, when he should have been going the rounds of
hospital patients, young Paul Ehrlich pumped a hypodermic needleful of methylene blue into the veins of a living
rabbit and observed with excitement that the bright color
appeared only in the nerves of the animal. Others had seen
this curious phenomenon, but his fertile brain suggested

ideas that kept him for years alternately synthesizing new chemicals in test tubes and experimenting with their effects upon animals.

"If methylene blue acts only on the nerves," he reasoned, "maybe it will kill pain without in any other way affecting the animal."

That idea was quickly blasted by a few simple trials. But he continued with the notion of hooking up a good narcotic with this dye that acted selectively on the nerves. It took years to convince this persistent searcher that this hooking-up business was not so easy as it seemed, but during these studies he also became convinced that a chemical could be synthesized that would kill all invading microbes. He dreamed of the drug of drugs, his glorious *"therapia sterilans magna,"* which would utterly abolish all germ diseases.

Ehrlich was well into middle age — a fumbling crackpot who was neither a good chemist nor a clever bacteriologist, so his professional brothers considered him — when he made a dye of the azo family that actually killed the germs of sleeping sickness. In 1909, by hooking arsenic into an organic group that acted selectively on the wicked spirochetes of syphilis he made salvarsan, the famous "606."

These discoveries fell short of the universal germ-killer, but they inspired renewed hope. Quite aside from their direct benefits in combating two of the deadliest of diseases, they founded the whole new science of chemotherapy. Hundreds of chemists and bacteriologists attacked this problem with freshened enthusiasm. For years the results were a series of failures.

While Paul Ehrlich was painstakingly combining arsenic with complicated organic compounds, Paul Gelmo, working for his Ph.D. degree at the Vienna Institute of Technology, was synthesizing a new coal-tar derivative. The new chemical was para-aminobenzene sulfonamide, which we know as sulfanilamide. In his thesis, published in 1908, he described it in detail. This compound and this date, too, are important. His full publication made impossible any subsequent patents on this chemical.

Exactly what happened to sulfanilamide from 1908 to 1932 is only to be found in the notebooks of workers in the laboratories of the German Dye Trust, original documents which any research organization keeps in the safe. Patents give us some hints of progress. A year after Gelmo's paper one patent was issued to Dr. Heinrich Hörlein and assigned to his employers the Bayer Company. It covered a brick-red dye of the sulfonamide group derived from Gelmo's sulfanilamide. Maybe it is significant that Hörlein was not a dye chemist, but head of pharmaceutical research. Other dyes of this group appeared from time to time, and other dye-makers experimented with them, but while exceedingly fast on fabrics they never made much of a stir commercially.

On Christmas Day 1932 another patent for a dye made from sulfonamide was issued, but nobody twigged its significance even though the German patents were assigned in the United States to the Winthrop Chemical Company, a medicinal subsidiary of the German Dye Trust. Furthermore, in this country the new compound was trade-named Streptozon, which might suggest to a hawk-eyed chemical sleuth that it was a germicide to be used against the streptococcus.

Next year the name was changed to Prontosil, but not till three years later, 1935, did a paper appear over the distinguished signature of Domagk, who reported 100 per cent cure of streptococcus-infected mice by use of this drug. This was stunning news. Strep germs are famously fatal to mice and such results were phenomenal. Soon medical journals began printing equally sensational stories of cures by Prontosil against all sorts of streptococci infections, pneumonia, meningitis, septic sore throat, wound infection, and other dangerous, difficult diseases.

Then a very dexterous French chemist, Fourneau, who delights to solve German chemical mysteries, teamed with a smart Italian bacteriologist, Levaditi, working together in the Pasteur Institute, Paris, pricked the Prontosil bubble. They proved that this complex chemical broke down in the human system into its simpler, constituent parts. The really efficacious part was the old, unpatentable sulfanilamide.

It is not unlikely that the Germans had known this a long time, and it has been charged that they held up, hoping to get a compound that would be as effective as sulfanilamide and still patentable. It is ironical that for all their skill and experience the German chemists persisted in following a wrong lead, working towards the azo dyes. Several improved sulfonamide compounds, or, as we have come to call this group, the sulfa-drugs, have been found among the thousands possible. Not one has come from German laboratories.

It should be an antidote to our common American belief in German chemical omnipotence to know that most recent progress has come from American researchers. Sulfapyridine was discovered independently in France by Poulenc Frères and in this country by Drs. Crossley, Roblin, and Northey of the American Cyanamid Company. They also found sulfathiazole, sulfaguanidine, most useful in intestinal infections, and the sensational sulfadiazine. The latest comer, succinyl sulfathiazole, was found by Ellis Miller and M. L. Moore in the medical research laboratories of Sharp & Dohme, Philadelphia.

Since the early part of 1937, when the extraordinary therapeutic value of sulfanilamide first came to the attention of the medical profession, a vast research and investigational work has been initiated covering new drugs in this field. Some leading drug houses and manufacturing-chemists have made large appropriations, in time and money, to research and development — including not only the synthesis of enormous number of sulfa-drugs, but also the pharmacological examination of all those which gave promise of therapeutic value, together with the clinical investigation necessary before acceptance by the Federal Drug Administration and the medical profession — and have carried through these results into final large-scale plant production. Other houses concerned themselves only with the production problem.

At the very start the American Cyanamid Company increased the staff of its chemotherapeutic research division, dividing the work among the Stamford laboratories, the Lederle laboratories at Pearl River, and the pharmaceutical laboratories at the Calco Division in Bound Brook. At all three points most of the time available to the development of new products was devoted to the sulfa-field. They did their own pharmacology or animal work and carried through to the clinical stage. At the same time the Calco Division of Cyanamid followed a constant program of manufacturing development and has been an important producer of all five of the principal drugs in this field, sulfanilamide, sulfapyridine, sulfaguanidine, sulfathiazole, and sulfadiazine.

Partly through connection with the English firm of May & Baker and also of its own research and development, Merck & Company has from the start been an important producer of sulfanilamide, sulfapyridine, and sulfathiazole. E. R. Squibb & Sons has taken a very active interest in several of these drugs, has contributed much in the pharmacology and clinical work, and, while not essentially a bulk manufacturer of products of this sort, has been an important producer of at least one of the sulfadrugs. Sharp & Dohme contributed much by way of research, pharmacology, and clinical work, and has been an important distributor, but has not undertaken large-scale production.

Other pharmaceutical houses, such as Lilly, Abbott, and Parke-Davis, have contributed both to the investigation work and also, to some extent, to production. Monsanto was an early producer of sulfanilamide and later, at the request of the Government, not only made substantial expansions in this plant, but also went into the production of sulfathiazole.

Furthermore, the War Production Board, in an effort to meet the combined requirements for military and civilian needs with the use of the minimum amount of critical material, has arranged production of both sulfanilamide and sulfathiazole in a number of smaller plants where conversion of existing equipment from nonessential uses could readily be made.

Making a sulfa-drug is not like punching out so many tin whistles. You guess this when you know that the correct chemical name of sulfadiazine, the sensational youngster of this remarkable family, is para-aminobenzene sulfon-amidopyimidine and its chemical formula is $C_{10}H_{10}N_4O_2S$. You become quite certain of it when you learn that this drug is prepared by "condensation of 2:aminopyridine with acetyl-sulfanilyl chloride and a subsequent hydrolysis followed by final purification by crystallization." The ingredients of this neat little recipe are not to be picked up at the corner delicatessen even with a ration coupon. Each step in the synthesis of such complex organic compounds takes a lot of special equipment and expert knowledge.

The expansion of the nation's sulfa-drug production, as planned by E. W. Reid and D. P. Morgan, chemical experts of the WPB, and checked by Major Purinton, required a lot of special apparatus — steam-jacketed kettles, stainless-steel evaporators, copper piping, and whatnot. Accordingly, the chemical companies resorted to one of their familiar experiences which have had much to do with their remarkable ability to squeeze unbelievable quantities of chemicals through all sorts of bottlenecks.

After they find what equipment and materials can be bought, additional plant capacity is improvised out of what may be begged, borrowed, and stolen from the existing plant. By modifying this and twisting that about, a new operating-unit is thus pieced together. Such a patch-work job is frankly an emergency makeshift, but it is not necessarily unsound. The flexibility of chemical processes is proverbial. There is hardly one of the 4,000-odd different chemicals made commercially that cannot be produced from some alternate raw materials and by several optional processes. For this reason competition in chemicals is bitterly keen, and research for the cheapest materials and processes with the best yield is as necessary for a chemical company as a set of double-entry books. By the same token it is just about as easy to get and hold a chemical monopoly as to capture a greased pig.

This everlasting juggling of materials and equipment is even a regular feature of large sections of the chemical industry's everyday operations. A dye manufacturer makes and markets 200 or more different coal-tar colors, many of them in several shades and various concentrations. A dozen may be tonnage products, but the demand for most is only a few hundred pounds. A day's run often turns out a year's stock. Accordingly, the equipment of a modern dye plant is like a gigantic set of Tinker-toys in which elaborate reaction vessels, filter presses, evaporators, driers, and whatnot are switched about. A bride settling her first drawing-room has nothing on a chemical engineer.

Such pliancy has its drawbacks, but it keeps chemical people — in the laboratory, in the plant, in the office — all awake and on their toes. If they fall into a rut they might as well slip into a quiet grave. In our chemical war effort this alertness of men and flexibility of materials have performed wonders of production that keep the ammunition passing to all parts of the chemical front.

In the sulfa-drug war program it was not always easy to meet the Surgeon General's specifications for the size of the granules of sulfanilamide and at the same time to supply his stepped-up requirements. Nevertheless, there were good reasons why this drug should not be delivered to Army surgeons in the form of either too coarse crystals or too fine powder.

Back in May 1940 the same Dr. Long who flew to Pearl Harbor for Surgeon General Magee had stood up before the members of the American Drug Manufacturers Association assembled in the long low room beside the courtyard of the Greenbriar at White Sulphur Springs and given a fascinating résumé of sulfa-drug progress. He is a capital speaker, professional and explicit in matter, but crisp and light in manner, and his vivid account of what British Army surgeons were doing with sulfanilamide had his listeners on the edge of their chairs.

It was no news that by dosing a man with 10, 20, or 30 grains of this marvelous germ-destroyer all sorts of streptococcic infestations might be controlled, but to some medical men this seemed a roundabout method. Besides, the ill effects many patients suffered from heavy doses of this active germ-killer were only too apparent. A few bold experimenters wanted quicker, more direct action by dusting sulfanilamide into open wounds. Their colleagues shook their heads, but Dunkirk and the air blitz against London filled the hospitals with ragged, gaping wounds and crushed bones already invaded by the murderous bacteria. In so hopeless an emergency any chance of lifesaving was worth a trial. All the world now knows the wonder that was worked.

Dr. Long gave the drug manufacturers some technical details. Clinical tests in this country on accident patients had taught that for local applications the physical condition of the powdered drug is important. If the crystals are too large, they do not readily absorb and by acting as foreign bodies in the wound they delay healing. If, on the other hand, the sulfanilamide is in fine-powder form, it cakes so that its germicidal potency is lowered.

Acting on these experiments, the Surgeon General set up the standard that sulfanilamide must meet the 40–80 test. In other words, any material that was retained on a screen of 40-to-the-inch mesh and any that passed through an 80-to-the-inch screen must be discarded for surgical dusting purposes, though it might be pulverized and fed into the tablet-making machines. Only about 15 out of every 100 pounds of sulfanilamide as it came from the crystallizers passed between the 40–80 meshes. And the need for the dusting form made this proportion about as sensible as the old 50–50, one horse–one rabbit joke.

Manufacturers all over the country put the problem up to the chemists in their laboratories. They experimented with the crystallization operation, changing temperature and time and concentration, varying all these in infinite combinations. Doctors reported that the dusting-powder served as well if the limits were stretched to 30–80, which let more than half the sulfanilamide pass inspection. Still these proportions did not begin to balance the production schedule.

One Saturday afternoon a little group of Monsanto production and research men conferred on this problem. It was the kind of little headache that must be treated after hours; yet somehow it must be cured, for an unbalanced production is something that, given time and big quantities, can work into a wicked jam.

Somebody had suggested compressing the fine powder, grinding and resizing it. They tried it out. The resulting crystals were not so shiny, but apparently the dullness would not affect their usefulness. A couple of days later Lynn Watt met General C. C. Hillman, who has charge of the Army's medical specifications, on the train Washington-bound and told him the story. They wired for samples, which were resubmitted to Dr. Long for testing at Johns Hopkins. Four days later came an approval, and inside the week the new granulated form, sifted to meet the original 40–80 test, was being shipped.

And here is how Major Purinton's questions — how much? how soon? — have been answered by the American chemical industry:

	1940		1943	
	Pounds	*Price*	*Pounds*	*Price*
Sulfanilamide	543,800	$1.35	4,000,000	$1.00
Sulfathiazole	91,907	14.50	1,350,000	3.50
Sulfapyridine	102,196	14.89	350,000	5.00
Sulfaguanidine	——	·	500,000	5.50
Sulfadiazine	——		2,000,000	8.50
Total sulfa-drugs	737,903		8,200,000	

Boost in pounds and cut in price, that is a record half a dozen American chemical companies — the Calco Division of American Cyanamid, Merck, Cincinnati Chemical Works, Monsanto, Abbott Laboratories, Lilly, Squibb, and Winthrop Chemical Company — made upon their own initiative and without subsidy. There are no Government-owned, industry-operated sulfa plants.

It is a record that reveals the characteristic lowering of a chemical price as production rises, an achievement born of technical experience which increases yields and improves quality and of the economics of continuous operation under automatic chemical control. It is a war record, too, for on every battlefront sulfa-drugs are ammunition as important to victory as powder and bullets. We are not going to win this all-out war with the remnants of an army.

In a steaming Asiatic jungle an American marine creeping through the giant ferns suddenly crumples, a sniper's bullet through his groin. Out of the frozen Arctic mists a shell fragment fired from a marauding submarine knocks an American sailor to the destroyer's deck, a jagged hole in his chest. Among the dusty alleys of an African town an American soldier gets his man, who in one desperate, last lunge thrusts his bayonet into the Yank's side. In swamp or desert, on the sea, in the air, whenever an American fighting man is wounded he is at once set upon by a myriad of enemies as ruthless as the Nazi, more treacherous than the Nip.

But he is not now defenseless against these invisible enemies who in all past wars have been so much more deadly than bullets and bayonets. In his battle kit are two powerful weapons: a little packet of white crystalline powder, sulfanilamide, and a little metal box of twelve sulfadiazine tablets. He has been carefully instructed how to stave off the attack of infection. He dusts the powder directly in his wounds. Every fifteen minutes he takes two of those tablets. He is protected doubly, inside and out. He has enormously bettered his chances of rapid, permanent recovery.

Most of our sulfa-weapons have been wrought in American chemical laboratories. Quite properly the physicians get much credit for the new chemotherapy. Yet before the first doctor takes a new chemical drug to the acid test of the clinic, highly trained bacteriologists have studied for months its effects on the micro-organisms in test tubes and under powerful microscopes, and skillful pathologists have fed it to rats and rabbits, or injected it into the laboratory animals, and scrupulously observed its effects on blood and bone and all kinds of tissue. Behind all are the chemists, often quite unhonored by the general public and unsung by the popular press, who with infinite patience and consummate technical dexterity have put together a brand-new combination of the atoms with which the doctors make their wondrous cures. But, after all, who remembers the name of Columbus's helmsman or the designer of Lindbergh's plane?

American chemists — and we should be proud of this feat — have given the medical corps of the Army and Navy weapons more than able to offset the enormously increased destructiveness of high explosives and bombs. The sulfa-drugs fight not only against the dangers of wound infection, but they combat gonorrhea (ancient curse of all armies), dysentery, pneumonia, even burns, which with the increased used of liquid fuels and the menace of the incendiary bombs are now a major source of casualties. With these weapons military medical men know that untold hours of suffering will be spared, literally millions of lives will be saved.

CHAPTER IX

SAFETY FIRST, LAST,
ALL THE TIME

◇◇

A YOUNG officer in the Tank Corps wrote from North Africa: "I am a human pincushion, an up-to-date version of the old circus freak. In the Army fourteen months and I have been jabbed by the doctors forty-two times, on the average three times a month, or once every ten days, which to borrow a favorite phrase from Major Blank of our Headquarters Staff is 'high incidence.'"

Our Army doctors are taking no chances. Prevention is proverbially better than cure, and the doctors' obsession with preventing such an army of remnants as Field Marshal von Moltke pictured is scrupulous safety, first, last, and all the time.

In this safety campaign the most effective weapons are inoculation with serums and vaccines, both the antitoxins and the more recently perfected toxoids — hence the human pincushion. In the African theater officers and men get extra jabs, since typhus fever has been reported there, and one of the latest of these anti-germ guns is aimed straight at the tough and wicked typhus bacillus.

The theory of the serums and vaccines is simple. But their preparation is a complex, delicate feat in bacteriological chemistry. The results appear miraculous.

The first vaccine was discovered by an English country doctor, Edward Jenner, who with insatiable curiosity and infinite patience followed for twenty-five years the clue given him by a dairymaid who boastfully assured him: "Oh, but I can never have smallpox. I have had cowpox."

During the eighteenth century smallpox was one of the commonest diseases in England, so common that for a woman to have escaped pock-marks was a capital claim to beauty, and young Jenner learned very quickly that his professional colleagues considered this cowpox notion a yokel's superstition. On the other hand, he was practicing in the heart of a dairy region where this belief was firmly held by everyone throughout the countryside. Following the maxim of his teacher and lifelong friend, the great John Hunter, "Don't think, but try; be patient, be accurate," he began collecting evidence.

There was altogether too much material to work with and the evidence was flatly contradictory. No doubt but that the cow's teats and udders were afflicted with the pox and that these distinctive eruptions could be conveyed to the hands of milkers. It took him years to distinguish between true cowpox, which was comparatively rare, and a more prevalent, spurious pox. In the end he proved to his own satisfaction that the dairymaid was right, that true cowpox did confer immunization against subsequent infection by smallpox. The physicians were right too, for the more common spurious pox afforded no protection against the human form of the disease.

After years of study the time for a trial had come. On May 14, 1796, Dr. Jenner inoculated a lusty eight-year-old boy, John Phipps, with true cowpox from the hand of Sarah Nelmes, a milkmaid. Eight weeks later he inoculated the lad with true smallpox, and nothing happened.

This dramatic experiment, quietly performed by a modest, hard-working general practitioner in an English village, confirmed the common observation that once a person survives certain dread diseases he is henceforth immune to them. It came within the realm of possibility, therefore, deliberately to administer such immunity. There were some wild guesses about the whys and wherefores of these indisputable facts and a storm of angry protests was whipped up against this unholy and dangerous treatment, but the facts, as is their habit, eventually prevailed. Vaccination became common practice and smallpox has become an exceedingly uncommon disease.

Bacteriologists and biochemists were gathering together facts that began in time to make reasonable replies to the whys and the wherefores. A healthy animal body attacked by invading bacilli fights the invaders by creating antibodies in its blood.

Antitoxins are a special form of antibodies. In the particular cases of diphtheria, tetanus, and perhaps botulism, the disease germ excretes its toxin in the medium in which it grows. It produces a "soluble" toxin, and when this substance is injected in proper doses into an animal — a horse or rabbit, or sometimes a cow or sheep — the blood serum of that animal acquires the property of neutralizing the toxin just as an acid neutralizes an alkaline substance. The blood serum is said to contain "antitoxin."

When the serum of the immunized animal is later injected into a man ill with diphtheria or tetanus — and the principle applies somewhat less markedly to certain other diseases — the toxin of the disease is neutralized and the illness is controlled. Immunity produced in this way is called passive immunity. It is only temporary, for it depends upon the amount of antitoxin administered artificially and it lasts only so long as this antitoxin persists in the patient's bloodstream and tissues. It is unfortunate that few organisms which cause acute infectious disease in man produce soluble toxins and that the passive immunity has therefore such limited application.

Active immunity is quite different. The horse treated with toxin develops antitoxin by the activity of his own tissues. His immunity is permanent or at least can be easily restimulated by a tiny dose of toxin given later, even years later. The man immunized against typhoid or typhus or yellow fever has been taught by small doses of the infecting agent to manufacture his own antibodies (perhaps including antitoxins) against the disease. Once a patient is treated with the appropriate "antigens," antibodies develop and the patient is immunized usually for life. This immunity, however, tends to fall off in time, but it can be reawakened by additional "booster" doses of the specific antigen. This active form of immunity was what Jenner accomplished in his bold smallpox experiments, and similar bacterial suspensions were named vaccines from the Latin word for cow, *vacca*.

It has taken half a century of scrupulous experimenting to find the most suitable animal host; to develop the exacting technique of preparing the immunizing vaccines; to find the dose and the technique which will stimulate immunity without at the same time making the individual sick. Antigens are made from the bacteria or the virus or the toxin which causes the disease, and it is difficult to destroy the toxic or poisonous properties of these agents without at the same time interfering with their immunizing ability. And the horizons of this biochemical world are ever widening.

Only twenty years ago, for example, Dr. George Ramon, starting with work on the diphtheria bacilli and the antitoxins available to combat them, introduced a new idea into this scheme of safety first. It was a distressingly common event for diphtheria inoculations with the best vaccines to result in a serious case of the very disease the inoculations were designed to defeat. The reason was obvious: the serum contained not only the friendly antigens, but also the hostile toxins. Ramon and his assistants at the Pasteur Institute sought to separate the bad toxins from the good antitoxins in order to perfect a thoroughly reliable, safety-first immunization. After three years they succeeded. They treated the serum with formalin, which detoxified the toxin, as it were, and remarkably increased its antigenic activities by stimulating the immunized human body to manufacture its own antitoxins.

The first of the toxoids, as the improved Ramon antitoxins are now called, was a major discovery, but this energetic and practical French bacteriologist did not rest on his laurels. He applied his formalin purification process to tetanus antitoxin and after exhaustive tests with the horses of the French Army found that it was good. The dangerous tetanus bacillus, which causes lockjaw in man, also attacks domestic animals, whence its spores are spread, through manure, to the land. Here these spores lie for years until they are transferred to an open wound in man or horse or sheep.

Tetanus or lockjaw attacks the farmer, and especially the stockraiser; yet it took a deadly toll of soldiers in World War I, fought over cultivated fields that had been fertilized for centuries with barnyard manure. In the German armies 38 out of each 10,000 wounded contracted this terrifying disease and three out of four died. The British armies had only 15 tetanus infections per 10,000 wounded and lost only half. We did still better: two out of 10,000 casualties and but one in ten fatalities. Behind the figures is the story of wider and wiser use of tetanus antitoxin as the war progressed. Our AEF reached the infected battlefields only after the doctors had learned that they must not wait for the distressing symptoms of lockjaw to appear before using the vaccine — a clean-cut victory for the safety-first idea.

Like tetanus, the scourge of typhus is broadcast by war. The mere whisper that typhus is abroad sends shivers down the spine of the boldest general, for the tiny, flea-borne bacillus has defeated more armies and devastated more countries than all the most ruthless conquerors of history. There have been rumors of typhus in Russia, Poland, and Greece, as well as ugly stories of its deliberate cultivation. This dangerous contagion flourishes under unsanitary conditions and spreads like fire in a pine forest before a high wind. Till very recently the defenses against typhus were, putting it mildly, not strong.

This was not for lack of trying. For years chemists, bacteriologists, and physicians had waged war against this most devastating disease, but the campaign was not conspicuously successful. The germ travels on fleas and lice, and its most dangerous spreader is the rat. All the customary sanitary measures, and extermination of the hosts, did help in control. But nothing remotely resembling either a chemical cure or a vaccination had been found. Several years ago German chemists had an inkling that minute quantities of benzoquinone, a coal-tar chemical, acted quite effectively as a typhus inhibitor, and the Belgians ascribed the same action to the suboxide of carbon. Exceedingly active oxidants in the bloodstream seem somewhat to control this virulent bacillus and even sometimes to cure when administered regularly in minute doses.

When the invasion of North Africa was planned with foreknowledge that the region was infested with scattered, but light typhus epidemics, our Army Medical Corps had good reason to be thankful that less than five years ago an efficient, safe vaccine against this plague had been perfected. It had been a thoroughly American scientific triumph, discovered in a laboratory of the United States Public Health Service by a bacteriologist born in Indiana and trained at Johns Hopkins.

Dr. Herald Cox does not play up very well to his double role of scientist and hero. He is a stocky chap, well under forty, with nice eyes and a frank smile, wide awake but most diffident. He would much rather talk about the beauties of the Bitter Root Valley or fishing in the Rockies than tell how he discovered the first typhus antitoxin and then jabbed twenty-one successive doses into his own arm before he dared ask for a volunteer to help test the serum.

All this happened in 1938 at the finely equipped Rocky Mountain Laboratory of the Public Health Service at Hamilton, Montana. After four years at the Rockefeller Institute in New York City, Dr. Cox had gone out there to plunge into research on Rocky Mountain spotted fever. He was seeking a vaccine against the virus of this disease, which incidentally is closely akin to the virus of typhus. Spotted fever is by no means confined to the Rockies. It also occurs in the Appalachian ranges of the Eastern States. In the West its host is the female wood tick; in the East, the dog tick. There are about 1,200 cases in the United States each year with a savagely high mortality.

Following a technique devised by Dr. Ernest Goodpasture of Vanderbilt University, Dr. Cox was using fertile hen's eggs as a perfectly sterile medium in which to cultivate a spotted fever vaccine. He kept on trying for two years and had just about concluded that all the possibilities had been exhausted with only failures to record. Then one day, with an experiment all set up in a Maitland flask, he ran out of chick embryos. Rather than discard the experiment, he decided to try the yolk sac of some of the eggs in his incubator. He scored a ten-strike, for the results were astonishingly good.

From spotted fever to typhus is a short, logical step. The yolk sac affords immunizing toxoids for both diseases. After a series of animal tests and the plucky experiment on himself, Dr. Cox's two laboratory assistants, Bell and Hughes, were each given three doses. After that it was just good sense, typhus being what it is, to immunize the entire laboratory staff.

Within a year the first commercial production of typhus vaccine had been successfully prepared by the Lederle Laboratories at their plant out in the rolling hills near Pearl River, New York. A large-scale trial was much to be desired, and Dr. W. G. Malcolm, the research director, remembered a thick-set, swarthy Hungarian physician who had worked with them several years before and who was said to be in Rumania. An outbreak of typhus had been reported in Rumania, so Dr. Adolf Eichhorn was located and a generous working sample of vaccine dispatched to his address. Shortly afterwards Dr. Johan of the Cantazunzo Institute in Hungary cabled for a supply. Whatever came of these tests remains a deep mystery. A single letter, acknowledging the arrival of the typhus vaccine, came through from Dr. Eichhorn — then the Nazi blitzkrieg blotted out Central Europe. However, through the co-operation of the National Institute of Health a try-out was arranged in Bolivia.

The Lederle Laboratories went ahead. To handle so potent a virus in quantity was more dangerous than juggling high explosives. Accordingly, a separate building was erected. Here a "forbidden area" was set aside, into which no person who has not been immunized against typhus is ever permitted to enter. Swifter and safer methods of commercial production were devised. A tiny hole is drilled into the large end of an egg that has been incubated for seven days. Through this the deadly virus is injected into the very center of the egg close to the yolk sac. Within from four days to a week the embryo chick dies, and as soon as this is determined by the egg merchant's familiar candling operation, the yolk sac is harvested for its crop of immuniz-

ing vaccine. The technique established, Lederle began
building up an inventory.

Just about this time — that is, early in 1940 — a visitor,
destined to initiate an explosive expansion of vaccine production, called upon Dr. Malcolm in Pearl River and
talked a long time confidentially with the director. Together they checked capacities of output and discussed
probable needs of vaccines and serums against diphtheria,
meningitis, pneumonia, scarlet fever, gas gangrene, tetanus, and typhus. The last three, being distinctively war
diseases, particularly interested Colonel Currie.

"Gas gangrene," he said, "is one of the worst. Could you
put on 600 horses for gas?"

"That's right!" said Dr. Malcolm, exploding a cloud of
cigarette smoke, his pet way of assenting to anything that
has his approval.

"Looks like we must build some more stables and go in
for horse-rustling."

That suggestion meant more than doubling their number of horses, and there are now more than 1,000 horses at
the Pearl River laboratories. And so they went on through
the list of Lederle products. It was specifically agreed that
generous stockpiles of tetanus toxoid and typhus vaccine
should be accumulated. Other plans were made to dovetail with those made at all the other biological laboratories,
and the working basis of close co-operation with the Army
Medical Corps was laid down.

Today the Lederle staff is double in number what it was
when those plans were discussed before the war. Women
have long been employed at the delicate tasks of the bacteriological laboratory, where their dexterous fingers, sharp

eyes, and painstaking patience have been at a premium, and before the war they comprised half the staff. Now, since more than 450 of the 1,000 men have gone off into the active services, the women number three out of four. To the harassed management it seems that the local draft boards ought to know that safety first for the fighting men is war work as direct as loading shells or building submarines, and that corps of physicians, bacteriologists, biochemists, veterinarians, and even humble laboratory assistants cannot be recruited by a want advertisement in the evening paper.

"It does seem," said Dr. Malcolm a bit ruefully, "that they delight in collecting the choicest specimens from our little scientific menagerie."

He was voicing a sentiment widely held throughout all branches of the chemical industry.

"I wish you could tell me," said a plant manager down in Baltimore, "how to convince a draft board chairman that making alcohol is not being in the liquor business and that if we fall down on deliveries, a smokeless-powder plant shuts down."

Stretching the manpower in a chemical operation means spreading the know-how dangerously thin, and within the inner chemical circle this has often been the most pressing problem — and sometimes the greatest accomplishment.

The notable accomplishments in vaccine production by half a dozen biological manufacturers were undoubtedly encouraged by the foresight of the Army Medical Corps. Behind its ideal of prophylaxis by inoculation this branch of the service has a wealth of practical experience. The Army Medical School was once characterized by the eminent Dr. William Henry Welch as "America's oldest school of preventive medicine," and the Army Medical School Laboratories are probably the world's largest manufacturers of typhoid vaccine. In them are produced every "shot" used in the compulsory inoculations by Army, Navy, and Coast Guard, the enormous quantity of 84,500 ounces a year — and that was before Pearl Harbor!

In 1911 the United States Army was one of the first to require these typhoid inoculations. During the mobilization on the Mexican border we suffered but a single typhoid casualty — a teamster who had not been vaccinated. That impressive demonstration was clinched by the World War I record of only 1,572 cases. Had the typhoid cases been at the rate of the Spanish War, there would have been more than 500,000. And the present war will undoubtedly hang up a new, better record.

Since the day of the Army's first Surgeon General, Benjamin Rush, a versatile gentleman, patriot, and physician, signer of the Declaration of Independence and the first man to suggest that decayed teeth might cause other diseases, Army medical men have continued to make many important contributions to humanity. Who does not know of Major Walter Reed's work on yellow fever, or what General Gorgas and the Army doctors did for sanitation at the Panama Canal, in Puerto Rico, and the Philippines?

Pioneer American bacteriologist, an outstanding scientist, George Miller Sternberg, veteran of three wars, twice promoted for bravery in the field, was Surgeon General during the Spanish War period. We have already noted that Major Darnall, later Brigadier General, was an early leader in water purification by liquid chlorine. He served many years as professor of chemistry at the Army Medical School and did much for safe water in camps and the field.

Our Army was the first to undertake the large-scale anti-malaria work and was a pioneer in venereal-disease control. Colonel H. J. Nichols of the Medical Corps actually co-operated with Paul Ehrlich in the earliest trials of "606." Work on amoebic dysentery at the San Francisco Military Hospital, in the Philippines, and on the Mexican border won for Colonel Charles F. Craig an international reputation; and following the trail-blazing work of Colonel La-Garde on the infections of gunshot wounds, Lieutenant Colonel Calvin Goddard has been recognized as a world authority on medical ballistics, powder marks, and especially the microscopic identification of bullets fired from the same or different weapons.

These are but a few samples of many achievements by officers of the Medical Corps. They are sufficient, however, to show the tradition of the service and the skill and devotion of its personnel. The American soldier is the best paid, the best equipped, and the best fed; he is also the best-cared-for soldier on earth.

CHAPTER X

THE WORLD'S GREATEST
BANK

◇◇◇

HE was no ordinary man, that marine, and the moment he stepped into the Red Cross Headquarters at New London, Connecticut, I spotted him for a victim. His double row of ribbons, the service stripes on his arm, the sergeant's chevrons proclaimed a soldier of parts. He carried these emblems of his profession lightly yet with an air of true distinction, and among that conspicuously well-turned-out corps the angle of his cap and the set of his belt were swankily correct.

He walked straight to the registration desk, and the moment he spoke I wanted to put him on the air. To help the blood-plasma campaign the local radio station, WNLC, had given fifteen minutes at six o'clock and I was to interview a doctor, a nurse, and several blood donors to get across vividly the story of the greatest bank in the world, the blood bank. Surely this soldier would have a grand tale, if it could be coaxed out of him.

Later, as he was lying on a neat white cot slowly opening and shutting his fingers to stimulate the flow of blood from the vein in his forearm into the little sterile jar that

hung beneath, I spoke to him. He greeted my cordial in-
vitation to the air with a hearty laugh.

"You don't want me. I'd be scared pink. I never did have
the gift of gab."

"You seemed to be getting along all right with that
pretty nurse."

"Oh, dames is different," he declared with finality, and
I took another tack.

"You know this blood plasma is good stuff" — he nodded
— "and if you'll say so and tell why over the radio, maybe
you can persuade ten or twenty other people to become
donors."

This impressed him, and I went on. "We're not on the
air for an hour. At the Mohican they can mix a real rum
swizzle, so let's go over there, and we'll work up half a
dozen questions and answers that will really tell people
what an important thing this blood bank is."

In the little cubbyhole cocktail room he told why he was
willing even to face the devastating mike to help this
cause.

"I was in Guadalcanal," he said as casually as you might
mention downtown, "and early one morning a particular
pal of mine and me was on outpost duty in a coconut grove
beside the Matanikau River. We'd dug a couple of sweet
little foxholes, and come daylight we begin taking a few
pot-shots at some Nips across the river.

"A sniper must have spotted Jim. Anyway, he got winged
just as he was aiming to fire, and the bullet went through
his forearm, into his shoulder, and out the middle of his
back. Four wound stripes for one shot, as I told him, trying to cheer him up a bit. His arm was broken and his

shoulder a mess, so after trying to fix him up, I figured I better get him back to a dressing-station.

"Half-way back we come up with a couple of corpsmen and a stretcher" — his lack of detail was distressing, but evidently characteristic — "and I went on in with him, 'cause he looked pretty poor and I wanted to be sure he'd be O.K. The sweat was standing out on his forehead, but, funny thing, he kept saying he was cold as Christmas, him sweating and the thermometer flirting with 90. The minute the doctor sees him, he says: 'Um, bad case of shock.'

"That made me mad. I knew that guy, inside and out, for two enlistments, and I'd seen him take most everything from a quart of rye whisky neat to three Jap prisoners single-handed, so I bawls out the medico. 'Shock, hell!' says I. 'Jim ain't shocked, not if the Japs blow up this whole God-forsaken island.'

"That little red-headed doc pays no attention to me. All he says is: 'Plasma!' and he goes to work cutting off Jim's shirt with a pair of shiny, crooked scissors.

"A corpsman comes out of their tent, tearing the wrappings off a tin can, and he takes out a couple of bottles — one was a cream-colored powder, that's the dried blood plasma, and the other's labeled 'Distilled Water,' with a roll of rubber tubing and a needle on the end. He mixed the powder in the water, and the doc jabs the needle into Jim's arm, just like they did to us over there when they were taking our blood, only they give him the water with that plasma powder dissolved in it.

"All the time the doc was working, and suddenly he says to me, without looking up: 'I know this boy's no jitterbug, and when I said shock I meant shock, but I don't mean

what you think. It makes no difference how much nerve
he's got, it seems to make little difference how badly he's
wounded, if he gets shock, he just fades out. Seven out of
ten of them do, unless we can get them a plasma transfusion.'

"It didn't make sense to me, but I've seen it with my
own eyes! Jim was out cold by this time, breathing short
and quick, but almost as soon as they took that needle out
of his arm he quiets down and the color starts coming
back in his face. In about a minute, believe it or not, he
opens his eyes and when he sees me he says: 'Hi, Broncho,
gi' me a cigarette.' And then I knows he's O.K.

"I never was a prize Sunday school pupil," he continued
earnestly, "but, sir, I give you my word, I've seen a guy
raised up from the dead, and — well — cripes, that's why
I'm for this blood bank."

He made a wonderful broadcast. He certainly put over
what blood plasma means to the boys out on the frontline.
He made vividly clear its tremendous life-saving powers
in cases of shock, that strange danger in which, sometimes
without serious bleeding, the amount of blood in the cir-
culatory system shrinks miraculously, causing faintness
and chill, exhaustion and death.

Following him one of the nurses explained what happens to the blood in its transformation into the wonderful life-preserving powder. From the vein of the donor it
is collected in a sterile jar. This is a closed system, so that
no air touches the precious fluid, which is sealed quickly,
stored in refrigerated cases, and hurried to the manufacturing laboratory. In its original container the blood is
centrifuged, that is, spun rapidly round and round, and

as cream is separated from milk in a separator, so the cellular matter, chiefly the red and white blood corpuscles, is driven to the bottom so that the clear blood plasma at the top may be drawn off.

The serum from 15 or 20 individual jars is now pooled — important work — so that it may be used with any blood type, and it is then divided into units of 300 cc., or about two-thirds of a pint. These units are quick-frozen at 40 degrees below zero in a mixture of dry ice and acetone and dried under vacuum to less than one per cent of moisture. Each is finally sealed in a can and packed within a vacuum with the bottle of sterile water, the needle, and necessary tubing, ready for instant use.

Plasma preparation can thus be described quite simply. In operation, however, it is not so simple. The raw material is most delicate, a delectable home for the bacteria that swarm in the air; and since the end product will be injected right into the bloodstream, it must be absolutely perfect. Skillful handling in the shortest possible time and minute controls over centrifuge speed, temperatures, and timing are all vital. As usual, these were evolved by long experiment and tested by many trials.

Years before anyone suspected the inner upset in the body's blood balance caused by shock, doctors had watched hundreds of thousands of men die from loss of blood. Naturally enough, the idea of transfusing blood had for centuries been a tempting prospect to physicians helpless by any other means to increase quickly the supply of this vital fluid in their patients' bodies. A lot of very ancient mumbo jumbo about the mystic character of human blood shackled progress in this direction till about three hundred years ago a few hardy, questioning surgeons dared to do a little experimenting. Results were baffling. Sometimes the patient was immediately and obviously helped. Sometimes he was thrown into convulsions and died as if poison had been administered. Nobody could foretell which would happen and no one could guess why. Blood transfusion remained a desperate last resort, literally a kill-or-cure expedient, until 1900, when a young Viennese physician, Karl Landsteiner, found that not all human blood is identical and that if the transfused blood did not match that of the recipient it would cause clotting, which was frequently fatal.

It required patient laboratory work to solve this puzzle, to identify four blood types and determine their various incompatibilities. One in ten of us belongs to Type I, universal recipients, in that these can receive blood from all types, but can give theirs only to those in their own group. Type IV is the opposite, universal donors, but able to receive only blood of its own type. This type is represented by about 43 per cent of the people. The other numerous group is Type II, which can give to Types I and II and receive from Types II and IV. The smallest group, Type III, 7 per cent of all adults, can give blood to Types I and II and take blood from II and IV. In practice all this is not so tangled as it reads, and being perfectly definite knowledge it made blood transfusion safe and effective. But it was still inconvenient.

Patients and donors had to be typed, and typing has been made quick and simple by Arthur F. Coca, a cheerful little man, a great joker, who probably still wishes that his youthful ambition to be a great concert pianist had been fulfilled, but who instead has been hailed as "the American father of allergy." Dr. Coca, who spent most of his years as professor of immunology at Cornell, by treating the blood of rabbits with human blood perfected a technique of typing so easy that it is done for every man in the Army and his blood type recorded on his identification tags, just in case.

Nevertheless, the donor-to-patient operation was of necessity clumsy. It made transfusions on the field of battle, or even in the advanced dressing-stations, where the need was greatest, just about as practical as giving every soldier his favorite dessert for dinner every day.

A great advance was scored early in 1916 when Drs. Peyton Rous and J. R. Turner of the Rockefeller Institute discovered that human blood, preserved with sodium citrate, might be stored a month and safely used in transfusions. That was the birth of the blood-bank idea. It was given a severe test when another Rockefeller Institute physician, Dr. O. H. Robinson, hurried to France, collected blood of various types, which he stored in makeshift, portable iceboxes, and began treating the desperately wounded with this preserved blood.

These transfusions worked seeming miracles and they suggested to an English Army surgeon, Captain Gordon Ward, that the dangers and difficulties of transfusing whole blood might all be done away with if only the plasma — that is, the liquid portion of blood freed of the red and white corpuscles — were used. Not till after the war was this sensible suggestion even given a trial.

During the early '20's a number of physicians and pathologists all over the world began testing out this plasma idea. It worked, and they began reporting in staid medical journals dramatic stories of lives saved by experimental human plasma when no donor of the correct type could be found for an orthodox transfusion. Because few physicians cared to risk the new method, it was several years before sufficient "clinical evidence" accumulated to demonstrate that plasma was safe and effective and that it clicked with every type of blood. The first published case history, by Dr. Percival Nicholson, appeared in the *American Journal of Pediatrics* in 1934.

Until 1940, however, the almost sole reliance was on preserved whole blood, which, following the lead of the Cook County Hospital in Chicago, hospitals here and abroad collected and stored on ice for emergency transfusions. In Russia the bank idea was carried a step further when blood withdrawn from persons killed in accidents was successfully used in transfusions, death thus defeating death.

Plasma had one great initial advantage over preserved blood: it could be used with any type. And another advantage was learned: plasma could be frozen, and it was discovered that frozen plasma did not lose its potency and that it could be kept practically indefinitely.

In a Philadelphia suburb, Glenolden, this life-and-death subject of frozen serums had for several years been the object of exhaustive researches aimed to make the distribution of vaccines and antitoxins to the medical profession simpler and less expensive. You are familiar with the neat little white ice chests labeled "Biological Products" that used to stand in the drugstores. They were good display stands, suggesting hospital sanitation and efficiency and all that, but this was merely making a virtue of necessity, since the proper preservation of serums demanded that they be kept under these exacting, if attractive conditions. With all these precautions, however, serums had to be dated to mark the limit of their safe use, and continual replacements of the pharmacists' stocks had to be made, a troublesome and costly process. Under such conditions it did not pay every drugstore to carry vaccines and anti-toxins, so that they were not universally available. All this machinery and waste kept the price of these valuable se-rums at a comparatively high level.

In truth, the Mulford Biological Laboratories of Sharp & Dohme, one of the oldest and largest makers of biologi-cal products, had great incentives to find better, more con-venient, cheaper methods of preserving their delicate products. Freezing was a rather obvious step in the right direction, and the Sharp & Dohme staff accumulated ex-perience with this new technique and learned a great many facts about its causes and effects.

This same problem of stabilizing and preserving serums had been approached from the physician's point of view by Dr. William J. Elser, then of the Cornell Medical School, and he contributed the nub of the idea of drying them. Powdered serum, he reasoned, should be safe and stable for years. In the Glenolden laboratory Dr. Elser's idea was translated into a practical process. The two ideas of freezing and drying were combined; after rapid freez-ing the water is drawn off from the frozen serum by a vacuum pump. This technique, with some modifications, was applied successfully to blood plasma.

At last here was the perfect "gold standard" for the

blood bank. The financial ideals of a medium of exchange that the yellow metal is supposed to fulfill — stability, availability, portability, and universal applicability — were met for the medical world by powdered plasma. It could be collected at any time from any type of donor, processed, and then stored in any climate even under rather unfavorable conditions. Complicated direct transfusion and the clumsy icebox methods of preserved whole blood or liquid plasma had all been abolished, and as if by magic it became possible to infuse invigorating vital fluid into the shrunken veins of shocked, burned, and bled patients almost anywhere, at any time. Blood transfusion had moved right up to the firing-line of battle and to the reeling, sea-swept decks of the smallest destroyer.

The Army and Navy recognized this at once, and both took a lively interest in the development of mass-production methods which were initiated at the Mulford Laboratories and developed largely in the Sharp & Dohme plant. On October 17, 1941, when the destroyer *Kearny* on the North Atlantic patrol, some 350 miles off Iceland, was ripped and staggered by the blow of a torpedo from a German submarine, the Navy was ready.

Called by radio, a seaplane swept in close and dropped by parachute three floating, watertight boxes, each containing two small bottles — cream-colored powder and pure water — and the first American casualty, Chief Boatswain's Mate Frontanowski, was snatched from the fatality list. Amid the wreck and ruin of Pearl Harbor it was a liquid-plasma bank collected thanks to the persistent enthusiasm of a civilian doctor, Forrest Joy Pinkerton, that cushioned the dreadful shock and saved hundreds of

BLOOD BANK IN ACTION.

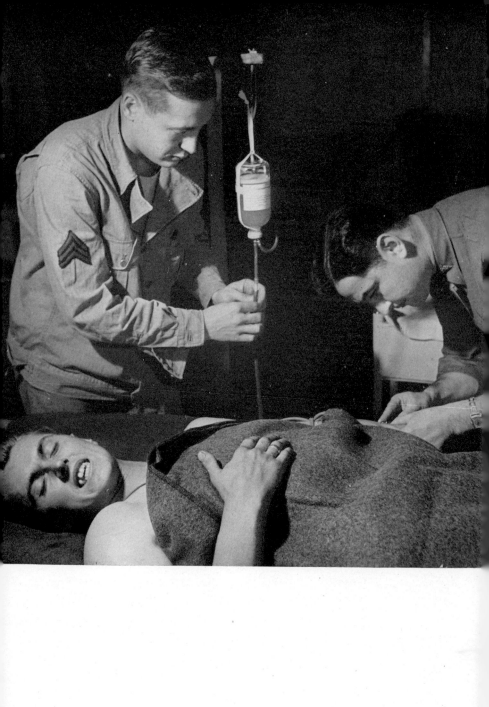

lives, but within forty-eight hours dried plasma, prepared 6,000 miles away in the Philadelphia suburb and flown to Hawaii, came to follow through the rescue work.

Already the building of the greatest bank in the world had begun, for the Red Cross had been enlisting donors for the British blood bank. The freezing and drying technique perfected by Sharp & Dohme went into large-scale plasma production. Actual declaration of war electrified this whole effort.

The Red Cross organized donor centers in leading cities and supplemented them by mobile units that kept prearranged schedules, receiving blood donations, packing them in refrigerated containers, shipping them off that same night to the manufacturing laboratories. To the original preparation unit were added the Lederle Laboratories, Pearl River, New York, Abbott Laboratories, Chicago; Eli Lilly, Indianapolis; Parke-Davis, Detroit; Reichel Laboratories, Kimberton, Pennsylvania; Cutler Laboratories, Berkeley, California; Ben Venue Laboratories, Cleveland; Hyland Laboratories, Los Angeles.

The Army and Navy stepped up plasma requirements from 15,000 to 200,000 units, after Pearl Harbor to 1,000,-000, early in 1943 to 2,500,000, and now to 4,000,000. So when you walk into a Red Cross blood-bank station — if you are a healthy American and have not yet become a donor, you have missed the most satisfying direct war contribution that you can possibly make — you give but a pint of blood, a painless, harmless gift, the raw material for a single plasma unit that will save a soldier's life.

Recently two new ideas in the use of blood have been developing. As it were, the blood bank has established two important branches. The first is a highly concentrated form of transfusion and the second a useful application of the formerly wasted red corpuscles.

A more concentrated plasma has been found in serum albumin, a protein substance in the blood which draws liquid from the body into the blood system, thus reversing the process which is one of the physiological consequences of shock, bad burns, and, of course, of excessive bleeding. The preparation of albumin, as worked out mainly by Dr. Edwin J. Cohn, professor of physical chemistry at the Harvard Medical School, is still a military secret, but it is being distributed now, chiefly to the Navy, in tiny vials with necessary equipment for administration in a hypodermic needle.

A unit consists of less than a single ounce of albumin in three ounces of normal salt solution. In transfusions one tiny unit of albumin is said to be as effective as two pints of plasma. On the other hand, it takes three and one-half pints of blood to produce that unit as against two pints of blood for the equivalent plasma. Its highly concentrated form, however, is especially interesting to the Navy, the commando and parachute troops, and the air forces. It is yet a dream, but it is possible that each soldier embarking on desperate undertakings may be equipped with an albumin outfit which he can use himself as easily and as safely as a diabetic does his insulin hypodermic. Then shock, the greatest killer of the battlefields, would be overwhelmingly defeated.

To many thrifty scientists the waste of the red and white corpuscles in plasma preparation seemed an atrocity. Here was priceless material, for the lack of red cells in pernicious anemia and the protective powers of the white cells in bacterial diseases are established facts. Already two good reclamation ideas have passed the discovery stage and become subjects of successful experimentation.

Dr. John J. Moorhead, an eyewitness of the medical miracles at Pearl Harbor, was inspired with the idea that this mass of blood cells, which looks very like a red paint paste, might be used to assist healing. With Dr. Lester J. Unger, plasma authority of the Post-Graduate Medical School and Hospital in New York, he packed a gaping nine-inch wound of a delirious patient with these blood cells, redressing it in the same manner every other day. The wound healed as if by magic.

In a dozen hospitals and as many laboratories, answers are being eagerly sought to a lot of questions this discovery has raised. Should the blood cells be applied as a paste or a powder? How long should the packing be left undisturbed? Are best results obtained if it is kept moist or allowed to cake over? Must the cells of the same blood group as the patient's be used? And how can this highly perishable material be kept any length of time without bacterial infection, which would be distinctly bad in open wounds? The physicians have not finally settled these problems yet, but they are well on the way to giving the military surgeons another potent weapon.

Late in 1942, in the Parke-Davis laboratories, a salt solution of the blood cells was prepared and after an accelerated testing in the pathological laboratories it was sent in January 1943 to several Detroit hospitals for clinical testing. These cell solutions naturally must be typed, but they seem to serve admirably for transfusions, and even to give superior results where loss of blood must be made good. More hopefully suggestive is their value in treating several different types of anemia.

Blood, dried blood plasma, blood albumin, and blood cellular material — the vital fluid has indeed become a new gold currency of life. In the postwar world the Blood Bank will vie with the Bank for International Settlements in serving mankind.

CHAPTER XI

BREAKING JAPANESE
MONOPOLIES

◇◇

WHEN the Japanese gobbled up most of the Pacific area they were following a well-thought-out plan that went much further than the spiteful satisfaction of ousting the Dutch from Batavia and humbling British pride at Singapore. It went beyond the obvious military objective of shoving the battlefront as many miles as possible away from the home islands. As the Japs knew very well, they were striking heavy economic blows.

They have grabbed, and are plundering, one of the world's richest storehouses of raw materials. Since possession is nine points in the law, they must hope to retain control of these headquarters of several most important natural monopolies.

Most of all the world's tin comes from this region. Rubber and quinine are famous monopolies of the Far Eastern plantations. Camphor, pyrethrum for flyspray, many other drugs and most spices, copra for coconut oil, hemp and sisal for rope, all these, and others less essential, are raw materials which all nations have drawn from lands

[147

now held by the Japanese. It must give the ersatz-hungry Nazis a bad case of envious indigestion to contemplate the array of spoils which their little brown partners in international piracy have scooped in so quickly and at such light cost. Comparison with their desperate grab for Russian wheat and petroleum must be very odious.

Nor is the prospect of that great Pacific storehouse pleasing to us. The Japs have cut us away from rubber, tin, and quinine, all essential war munitions not easy to replace. By the same token they have provided their own war machine with ample supplies of these necessities as well as with petroleum and big stocks of rice and vegetable oils for rations. From this surfeit of captured raw materials they are able to barter for goods they lack, as, for example, their trading of 80,000 tons of crude rubber for Russian high-test gasoline. Their brazen surprise raids have not only greatly strengthened their war position, but also put into their hands a number of high trump cards to be played at the peace table and the postwar economic conference.

For some time to come we shall hear a great deal about these Japanese-controlled raw materials. Several of them impinge dramatically upon the chemical front. These are entangled in the economic competition between natural and synthetic products, the historic battle of land and laboratory. Accordingly, they become involved in the delicate game of international trade versus national self-sufficiency. They will breed a flock of problems that will best be solved, not politically, but technically; not by politicians, but by chemists who are expertly equipped to appraise the real values of such materials.

When the Japs took over Java they deprived us of a munition of war vital in any tropical campaign. Without quinine the stoutest soldier is defenseless against malaria. The consuming fever throws him flat on his back, and when he crawls back to duty he is weak and ineffectual. Without quinine how could the Yanks ever dislodge the hardy little Nips from the infested jungles of Malaya, of Burma, of Indo-China, from all the multitude of islands of the South Seas, even out of our own Philippines?

So the Japanese generals thought. No doubt they planned it that way. But we are driving them out, doing that tough job in the most luxuriantly pestilent of all the malarial regions on the globe and with white troops from the Temperate Zone. And our casualties from malaria are not conspicuously high.

Malarial fever, with some 300,000,000 victims each year, is one of the most widespread of all germ diseases. It is also one of the most deadly. Nearly 100,000 persons die of malaria every day.

The disease is spread by mosquitoes, which throughout the tropics flourish the year round. In warm climates there is no closed season on the malaria germ. Over vast areas, even in certain sections of the United States, practically the whole population is infected. The wastage is terrific.

Furthermore, the life cycle of the micro-organisms that cause the familiar, recurring chills and fever has been devised with what seems diabolic ingenuity to hide its origin and to escape any interference with its successful completion. It was a capital scientific triumph to learn the secrets of this obscure disease. The wonder is that it did not exterminate us first. It would certainly have driven us out of all the tropical lands had it not been for the chance discovery by South American aborigines of a natural bark from which chemists learned to extract the first of all true chemotherapeutic agents.

Quinine had an appropriately sensational introduction to the civilized world. In the year of grace 1638 the beautiful and gracious Lady Ana, wife of the Count of Chinchón, Spanish Viceroy of Peru, lay in her great, carved, four-poster bed in the palace at Lima, grievously ill of a fever. In Loxa, a hundred miles away, a Jesuit missionary had brought back from the high Andes a strange reddish bark. His own life, he said, had been saved by it and he had been given the precious gift by the native medicine man, who had assured him that it would drive away that malicious demon who delighted to rack his victim with alternate chills and fevers. The priest was a friend of the local mayor, who was a friend of Dr. Juan de Vega, physician to the Viceroy's family. By swift Indian runner a little bundle of the bark was dispatched to Lima. The fair patient gulped down copious draughts of a nasty, bitter concoction of the pulverized bark in hot water, and miraculously the deadly grip of malarial fever was broken.

Grateful lady and smart doctor did a selling job that would do credit to any up-to-date advertising-agency. "Jesuit's powder," the pulverized bark of the tree which botanists call cinchona in honor of the beautiful countess, was a godsend to the malaria-ridden sections of Southern Spain. Its fame spread all over Europe.

Though it cured thousands, Europeans knew no more about the chemistry and therapeutic action of cinchona bark than did its tawny discoverers in the Peruvian jun-

gles. Not till 1817 was the riddle of its potency solved by
an industrious pair of French pharmacists, Pelletier and
Caventou. This successful partnership specialized in the
chemical mysteries of medicinal drugs. They had already
isolated strychnine from the deadly nightshade, and they
found that the similar active principle of "Jesuit's powder"
was quinine.

No longer did malaria patients gag over cupfuls of that
hot, bitter brew. The fever-bark's curative power was now
extracted as a white powder and administered in pills of
concentrated, definite doses.

Sixty years later, after Pasteur had found the microbes
and explained the nature of germ diseases, a French Army
surgeon, Alphonse Laveran, proved that malaria is caused
by a protozoon parasite and that quinine actually destroys
this micro-organism in the bloodstream. So was scored the
first triumph of chemotherapy, the discovery of a chemical
that selectively slaughters the germs of a given disease in
the body of a human being.

In the meantime cinchona bark had become big business. A worldwide market existed ready-made, and the
South Americans played it for a wee bit more than it was
worth. They exploited the source by greedily stripping
the bark, so that the great trees were killed off and what
seemed to be an inexhaustible supply was gravely depleted. They held up their customers by piling high export duties on top of fancy prices. This rapacity created an
opportunity which the thrifty Dutch seized.

Posing as an explorer with a hobby for collecting strange
butterflies and plants, Justus Hasskarl, botanist of the
Dutch East Indian Government, visited Peru. At the risk

of his life he smuggled out a hundred baby cinchona plants and a little packet of seeds. From this adventurous feat, after years of patient, careful work of selecting trees whose bark showed the highest quinine content, learning the best methods of cultivating, stripping, and curing, and developing processes to extract the quinine, the Dutch plantations gradually built up a virtual world monopoly.

It is poetic license to say that chemists have an inborn antipathy to natural monopolies. It is a familiar fact, however, that monopolists can seldom resist the temptation to raise the price of their products. Gradually that price becomes so high that eventually a smart chemist can reproduce the monopolized product or find a suitable substitute for it at a cost that shows a neat manufacturing profit.

That is why, at the time the South Americans were overplaying their bark monopoly, Professor Hoffmann suggested that if his bright student, William Perkin, could synthesize quinine, he would have accomplished something chemically and commercially worth while. In this effort Perkin stumbled upon the first coal-tar dye. But the work went on. Of late years the Dutch monopoly, though careful not to raise too big a price umbrella over possible competitors either natural or synthetic, has kept alive the long-deferred hope of duplicating the highly complex quinine molecule in the laboratory.

To this lure of the dollar the Germans have had the added incentive of national self-sufficiency. For years this has been one of their great goals, and synthetic quinine has long been sought by many German chemists. They must have chalked up an impressive list of failures, but about 1925, in the Elberfeld laboratories of the Dye Trust, they put together a new chemical, a sort of distant cousin by marriage to natural quinine, that apparently did things in the life cycle of the three deadly members of the plasmodium family of parasites which cause malaria. Appropriately they christened this new chemical plasmochin and sent it forth for testing.

Now the plasmodium germs do not lead a simple life. In fact, it is a highly double life, for these minute, one-celled organisms exist in two forms. One of these is asexual; the other consists of both males and females. They divide their labors, too, the asexual form doing its work in the red corpuscles of the human body while the sexual form carries on within the stomach of the mosquito.

Within the red corpuscle the asexual parasite divides, subdivides, and divides again till about twenty are so formed. Then the red blood cell bursts, liberating the crew, which immediately attacks other red corpuscles, and the dividing begins all over again. According to the species, this cycle takes from twenty-four to forty-eight hours, and it is when the new broods burst forth that the victim suffers the typical attack of chills and fever.

The male and female parasites do not attack the red blood cells, but float about in the bloodstream, waiting to attach themselves to the proboscis of a mosquito that bites their human host. From here the females work their way to the mosquito's stomach, where they hatch literally millions of baby plasmodia. These congregate in the salivary glands of the mosquito, ready for transfer to the blood of the first man their host bites.

It was soon discovered that plasmochin kills the sexual

form of malaria germs, but leaves unharmed the asexual
form which causes the chills and fever. Quinine, on the
other hand, works the opposite way, killing the asexual
plasmodia, but leaving the breeders unharmed. Quinine
plus plasmochin, therefore, should not only cure malaria,
but also control it. Still the Germans did not have a synthetic cure, so they went ahead with their search. In 1933
they found atabrine, which kills the asexual and in some
species even kills both the asexual and sexual forms of the
parasite. Here at long last it seemed was the chance at
least of prevention and cure with a single drug, the even-
tual possibility of ridding the race of the malaria plague.

Impressive medical evidence piled up for atabrine. It
was not available, however, in quantities such as the Army
and Navy would need in the event of war, and quinine
must still be the main reliance. So the Government accumulated a quinine stockpile sufficient for two years' domestic demand. To this could be added large stocks which
American pharmaceutical houses built up with an eye
upon Far Eastern eventualities.

Accordingly, we were not caught quite wholly unprepared, but with campaigns in the South Pacific and Africa
and the possibility of action in Southern Europe, the stocks
were far too small. A week after war was declared, priorities were placed on quinine, and a national roundup of
stocks from druggists' shelves was headed by Dr. Ivor
Griffith of the Philadelphia College of Pharmacy and Dr.
E. F. Kelly, secretary of the American Pharmaceutical Association. But as Rear Admiral Ross McIntire, Surgeon
General of the Navy warned, "The need for quinine becomes increasingly urgent as the number of men fighting

in malarious regions increases and the stockpile dwindles."

The plot of the Jap war lords was maturing as per schedule. We have extricated ourselves by means of a discovery made by the Japs' own ally and now at our command, thanks to exactly the kind of international patent pool which our own Department of Justice has been so assiduously trying to abolish. Chemists chuckle over a situation that so lavishly heaps irony on sarcasm.

After atabrine had been proved out, the I. G. Farbenindustrie transferred American rights in these patents to its American affiliate, the Sterling Products Company. Sterling, through its subsidiary, the Winthrop Chemical Company, began manufacturing. The Germans naturally supplied full technical information; equipment was designed and installed under their experienced direction; and actual production of atabrine along with invaluable, practical operating experience was acquired in this country prior to the war. The agreements with the I.G., under which these benefits had accrued, were broken by a consent decree at the insistence of the Department of Justice, and the Alien Property Custodian is administering the German-owned stock interest in these companies; but at its own expense Sterling Products increased its capacity to make atabrine by 4,000 per cent, and arranged through Harry S. Howard of the Harmon Color Works to make 60,000 additional pounds for an atabrine stockpile.

Lease-lend requirements, since England and Russia were as isolated as this country from the old Java source, began to be felt, so in the spring of 1942 James Hill, Jr., president of Sterling, sat down with George W. Merck and James Kerrigan to arrange an additional atabrine output of 300 pounds weekly by Merck & Company. It was a logical suggestion. Merck is an established fine chemical maker, with specialized experience in preparing alkaloids, and down in Virginia it had a beautiful new plant. At that conference it was agreed that the new production should be ready in October, and both companies went to work. Merck facilities combined with Sterling know-how had the new installation completed by the end of July and the first shipments beat the schedule by two months. Since that initial output in August 1942, the capacity of that Stonewall plant of Merck's has been multiplied tenfold.

Nevertheless, the search for true synthetic quinine, or a better substitute for it, still goes on. While there is no doubt that atabrine does things to the malaria parasite, unfortunately it also sometimes does things to its human host. Too frequently for comfort, continued doses have toxic effects which distressingly are often mental. As in the case of several of the sulfa-drugs, atabrine should therefore be administered only by a wise physician. The approved method of treatment for malaria is to stagger several days of atabrine doses with a day or so of quinine. Though medical men are learning more and more how to use this powerful drug most efficiently and with the least bad after-effects, the old hunt for a true active synthetic quinine is on with renewed gusto. It might prove to be one of the chemical triumphs of this war, for certainly the incentive is greater than ever before.

You would naturally suspect from quinine's chemical formula, $C_{20}H_{24}O_2N_2:3H_2O$, and its high molecular weight, 378.25, that it is complex, and it has proved a very tough compound for the organic chemists to synthesize. But they

are on a hot trail. Plasmochin and atabrine are both coal-
tar derivatives; the former from quinoline, the latter from
acridine. Having put them together, the chemists know all
about their structure and their chemical relationships to
the alkaloid quinine. Both these synthetics lack, as they
say, the quinuclidine heterocycle found in the natural
drug, which means that the researchers are not following
that trail in the dark or without good chemical clues. This
work is being pushed actively at the Rockefeller Institute,
the University of Minnesota, Penn State, the University
of Virginia, in the laboratories of two of the chemical companies — Dow and Monsanto — and of several of our important pharmaceutical houses. Seldom, if ever, has there
been such a wide, yet intensive chemical research.

In the meantime it can be no comfort to the Japanese
generals who planned the quinine coup to know that by
early spring 1943 three American chemical plants were
turning out atabrine at the rate of a quarter of a million
pounds a year, and the Nazi High Command must be positively discomforted by this news. This is worse news for
them than appears on the surface, for while atabrine apparently does things to malaria germs that even quinine
cannot accomplish, it is certain that it helps our acute shipping problem. A ton of quinine is sufficient to treat from
30,000 to 100,000 cases of malaria, whereas a ton of atabrine provides treatment for 600,000 patients, a neat saving of five-sixths of handling efforts and of cargo space.

While expense is not the prime consideration in protecting the health of our armed forces, we like to know that
the cost of treating malaria with atabrine is less than half
that of quinine. Thus, what the Japs planned as a slick

squeeze play in their war game has been turned into a double play for our side. With the prospect of a still better quinine substitute in the offing, any threat of a Japanese-controlled quinine market has lost its sting. Again the chemists have broken a powerful natural monopoly.

Another Japanese monopoly had already been smashed several years before the war. This is but another version of the familiar tale. Camphor is the gum from a tree that flourishes only in the Japanese-owned island of Formosa, and like all good monopolists the Japs ran the price up to their own profit. In fact, they handled this monopoly very adroitly and as far back as 1904 precluded any breaks by issuing an imperial decree under which it became an official, legal entity backed by the power of the Government.

So long as camphor remained a moth repellent and a cold inhalant people merely fussed over that Japanese monopoly, but did nothing serious about it. However, when camphor became an important industrial material, an essential ingredient in the celluloid-type of synthetic plastics, in motion-picture film, and in safety glass, then chemists had good reason to study this aromatic gum.

Beginning in 1900 half a dozen attempts were made to produce synthetic camphor in the United States. It could be done, but owing to technical difficulties that made the cost so high, the Japanese could well afford to cut the market out from under these adventurous chemical rivals. In 1931, however, the du Pont Company took over the chemical end of the Newport Industries and thereby acquired Ivan Gubelmann, an enthusiast for synthetic camphor prepared from pinene, a derivative of American turpentine. His new employers, once sold upon his process and being large users of camphor in their pyralin wares, went into the business seriously.

Once again the Japs played their old price-cutting tricks. The cost of the synthetic material was effectively competitive with refined camphor at 35 cents a pound, the normal price. When this was slashed by the monopolists, an appeal was made to the Tariff Commission, and a unique tariff agreement resulted.

"We agree," said the Commission, "that camphor is a necessity; that we should be independent of this controlled foreign supply; that you cannot meet their cut prices. Will you agree, if we give you adequate protection, to assure the nation of camphor independence?"

"That is our intention."

"Fair enough, but will you accept this challenge? We will recommend five cents a pound, providing that you will supply 25 per cent of all domestic consumption of camphor in 1933, 30 per cent in 1934, and 50 per cent in 1935 and thereafter."

The challenge — protection dependent upon production — was accepted and has been fulfilled handsomely. We must have more than 5,000,000 pounds of camphor a year. We need not get a pound of it from Formosa.

CHAPTER XII

CHEMISTRY IN POLITICS

◇◇◇

RUBBER has an economic background and a chemical history strikingly parallel to that of quinine. In this global war these great commodities are essential munitions, and our chief source of supply of both has been cut off by the Japs. But the parts played by rubber and quinine in our war effort have been conspicuously and significantly different.

The rubber tree, *Hevea braziliensis,* and the tree of the fever-bark, *Cinchona calisaya,* are both natives of South America: the former from the deep jungles of the Amazon river basin, the latter from the heights of the Andes. Both trees were greedily and recklessly exploited till the wild supply was gravely depleted. At the same time every advantage was taken of a growing, worldwide demand to advance prices right up to the breaking-point. Both trees were transplanted to the Far East, where they became important crops, mainstays of the plantation system upon which the prosperity of important Dutch and British colonies is based. By scientific breeding, painstaking cultivation, and skilled harvesting, the yields of latex and alkaloid were both increased almost unbelievably. The preparation of the product for the market was studied and perfected. Eventually production quotas were set up, and to prevent cut-throat competition the distribution of both products was controlled. In the end, two exceptionally effective natural monopolies evolved.

The United States has long been the world's greatest consumer of both rubber and quinine. For several years we have bought more than 650,000 tons of rubber gum and latex, more than 2,000,000 ounces of quinine and its salts. Since the cultivation of neither of these plants is commercially feasible within our borders, our dependence upon foreign sources of supply for both commodities has been absolute, and as our demand for them has grown steadily with the passing years our needs for them have become more and more imperative. War in the Pacific created twin crises.

Chemically, rubber and quinine are as unlike as coconuts and pecans, but both have been tough nuts for the organic chemists to crack. Both substances have roused the interest of many great scientists and each has been the subject of much research. Just as the alkaloid quinine was isolated years ago — by the two French pharmacists in 1817 — so the chemical basis of rubber, the hydrocarbon isoprene, a clear, colorless, unstable liquid with the formula C_5H_8, has been known a long time.

Isoprene was first identified as the parent substance of rubber gum by Greville Williams in 1860. Twenty-four years later Sir William Tilden, another English chemist, prepared it from turpentine and quite unwittingly hit upon the first synthetic rubber. He put some of his laboratory-made isoprene into a clear glass stockbottle on a shelf where the sunlight fell upon it each bright morning. Several weeks later he was astonished to find that the clear liquid, which boils even two degrees lower than the temperature of our own bodies, had been transformed into a sticky, elastic gum.

"Eureka!" shouted Sir William. "Synthetic rubber!"

He was quite right, but a half-century was to pass before anything approaching a practical rubber substitute was to come out of the test tube. However, his chance discovery led to a sound knowledge of the structure of the rubber molecule.

His sticky mess, so careful chemical analysis proved, was still C_5H_8, pure isoprene and nothing else. He reasoned, and rightly, that the marvelous transformation from liquid to gum could be explained only by assuming that the five carbon atoms and the eight hydrogen atoms were arranged differently. Tilden died without knowing what the difference is in the molecules of liquid isoprene and isoprene gum.

In the liquid the C_5H_8 molecules are all separate, moving freely in all directions, as the molecules do in any gas or fluid. In the gum the molecules are hooked together, linked end to end as one might make a chain of paper clips.

In their molecular structure, therefore, rubber and quinine are fundamentally different. Quinine is a product of the ring family, rubber of the long-chain group. The complex structure of quinine involves the hooking together of three distinct, six-sided benzene rings. In rubber, on the other hand, from 200 to as many as 4,000 isoprene molecules are linked into chains; the greater the number, the better the property of elasticity.

This long-chain formation is called by chemists polymerization, and the first attempts to make synthetic rubber were aimed at inducing the isoprene molecules thus to polymerize quickly, cheaply, and into the longest possible chains. The attempts were not very successful. However, numerous ways of polymerization were discovered, but even today, after tons upon tons of chemicals have thus been linked together to form the various rayons, nylon, and now the synthetic rubbers — all these, and many others, are composed of long-chain molecules — nobody has yet the foggiest notion of why and how this peculiar reaction of polymerization works as it does. Nevertheless, many compounds have been found that do polymerize and it has been discovered that two compounds may be polymerized together. Such co-polymers, instead of being like a chain of paper clips, have been likened to the homemade chains of popcorn and cranberries we used to festoon the Christmas tree.

Upon these foundations, laid down just before the last war, have been built the famous Bunas, storm center of our present rubber crisis. Buna S, backbone of our great synthetic rubber program, is a co-polymer of butadiene and styrene. Its production therefore involves three quite distinct, but necessarily interrelated operations, the production of the two ingredients and their polymerization together to form the synthetic elastomer. As every citizen and his wife and all the children now know, butadiene can be made from petroleum, alcohol, and sundry other raw materials, such as acetylene, and it certainly is no military secret that the competition among these different raw materials for the production of butadiene has been one of the big monkey wrenches thrown into the wheels of our synthetic rubber program.

That program promises to be the Teapot Dome of our World War II effort. Someday, no doubt, it will all be aired by a Congressional committee appointed, as was the Graham Committee of 1920, "to investigate the conduct of the late war." The selfish interests that pulled wires, the politicians who played their own sordid game, even the sincere idealists who made foolish mistakes, all will then be revealed. It is not yet the time for such a probing.

Nevertheless, our rubber needs are still critical, and already the postwar battle between natural and synthetic rubbers rises as a problem of international reconstruction. Therefore, because John Citizen and his family have been so bemuddled about a question of such prime concern to each of us, the hard lessons we are paying so dearly to learn might well be reviewed, simply in the hope that they will not be too quickly forgotten and that they may be applied in the future. Rubber is, and will be for several years, a red-hot issue.

Our present desperate plight for rubber is almost entirely unnecessary. We should never have been caught short, and, if woefully unprepared, we ought to have been able more quickly to obtain relief with synthetic elastomers.

Everybody knew Germany's frenzied effort to produce a satisfactory ersatz rubber. It was openly set up as Number One in the self-sufficiency campaign, and der Führer himself boastfully broadcast at the opening of the Berlin Automobile Show, February 1936: "Positively and forever we are free from foreign domination of our necessary supplies of rubber."

Rubber trees flourish no more luxuriantly in the United

States than in Germany. Since our rubber imports were ten times as great, we were more utterly dependent than the Germans upon the self-same foreign sources. Our rubber manufacturers sensed the sinister implications, both in peace and in war, of this dependency and back in 1937 they eagerly tested the samples of the first Buna rubbers and welcomed the visiting German chemists sent over by the I. G. Farbenindustrie in co-operation with Standard Oil of New Jersey, which had American rights to the I.G.'s synthetic rubber patents. American rubber companies made tires of Buna S and tested them. Here, at last, they all agreed was salvation from foreign control over the price and supply of their essential raw material, and they went to Washington to tell their story to the Army and Navy Munitions Board.

"This stuff is good," they said in effect, "but it will cost at first about three times as much as natural rubber. The petroleum companies would like to produce butadiene and at least two chemical companies are making styrene. We would like to build four polymerization plants of 100,-000 tons' yearly capacity each. But because of the cost it can't be done. In Germany the Government has simply ordered the tire-makers to use 10 per cent of Buna the first year and 25 per cent the second. What chance is there of Congress passing a law that would boost the price of tires from $8 to $14 in order to buy insurance against war with Japan? The only chance is for the Government, as a preparedness measure, to finance these raw materials and polymerization plants. Then we should be ready. We would have experience in making these synthetic elastomers and would have learned how to compound and

fabricate them. In case of a war emergency, to expand a
going output would be comparatively simple."

They talked themselves hoarse telling that story. They
brought experts, chemists, and accountants, to explain its
technicalities. Apparently many of their listeners thought
they were talking nonsense; others suspected them of trying to put something over on Uncle Sam. At last, after a
year, the Munitions Board, though it cut the four 100,000-
ton plants to four 25,000-ton plants, did give their proposal
formal approval. Then the National Defense Council took
over the preparedness campaign and the whole story had
to be told again.

Between early 1940 and December 7, 1941, the synthetic rubber program, having already been before the
Munitions Board and the Defense Council — both approved a 100,000-ton experimental program — was handled by the Reconstruction Finance Corporation, Office
of Production Management, the War Production Board,
the Defense Plant Corporation, and finally the Rubber Reserve Company. Two in turn approved the 100,000-ton
project. The last, just before Pearl Harbor, suspended the
entire synthetic plant building program for one year.

All the heroes of our voluminous detective fiction cannot now find the murderer of rubber preparedness. But the
lesson is plain. Seven official bodies handled the problem.
Not one ever had authority to approve a plan, provide
funds for its execution, and see it through to completion.

Neanderthal man learned with disgust that too many
cooks spoil the broth. But we smart moderns have ignored
this primitive wisdom for nearly two years, ignored it in
the face of a critical shortage of a raw material vital to

SYNTHETIC RUBBER PLANT.

our accustomed way of living and our military might.

If there ever was a big, tough, straight technical job, it is the quick production of Buna S from pilot plant to 700,000 tons. It happens to be the greatest, most radical industrial chemical development ever undertaken. From Washington to Crossroads Corners very few people have grasped just what that means. Pre-eminently it is a job for the chemically trained men. Especially is this true since it involves a number of untried processes, so that there is no established best method that might be safely approved by anyone.

Remembering Watson Davis's warning that the duration of this technological war will be measured by the promptness and completeness with which the General Staff and Congress come to accept the advice of technical experts, I went straight to one of our most competent rubber technologists.

"Tell me," I said to this man who has made experimental batches of many synthetic rubbers and who five years ago helped fabricate and test several hundred tires of Buna S, "tell me, off the record and as an old friend, how would you have handled our rubber problem?"

"I should have called together the heads of all companies interested and asked them to nominate a technical committee. If you want good men and true, don't appoint them; let the industry itself name them, and you will then get competent men all will trust.

"Subject to review by that group of experts," he went on, "I should tell every company to get their product into commercial production as quickly as possible. I would give every encouragement and reasonable financial help to any

honest group whose process seemed promising, but I
should make them all set up their own quotas and put the
job up to them. To keep the various raw materials and the
polymerization plants in line, plans ought to be subject to
review, but I would not make the fatal mistake of drawing
up standardized plans for buildings or for processes.

"Within a year, had the companies been left alone, we
should have been able to judge pretty well which are the
cheapest, most available raw materials and the most efficient processes. Then, and not until then, I should set up
a definite production program. On paper, this doesn't read
as well, but had this basic plan been adopted, and followed, we should have more rubber today and also a great
deal more sound technical information."

A little informal Gallup poll of executives and technicians who have been up to their ears in the rubber mess
unanimously confirmed this diagnosis. Instead of a frankly
experimental, competitive, cut-and-try plan, a definite program, with its implied promise of definite production, was
adopted. During the first five months of war our synthetic
rubber production was boosted and boosted on paper, and
since the Baruch report it has been cut and cut again. And
every change, up and down, has been accompanied by
costly, discouraging switches in plans and priorities.

Behind the scenes grisly stories are told of the waste
and confusion caused by a constantly shifting, technically
ignorant, irresponsible bureaucratic control. One example,
no more horrible than many others, suffices. One company,
its plans approved and priorities arranged, had bought
land and laid down its basic utilities (roads, railroad sid-
ings, water mains), when without warning it was ordered

to suspend all work and submit plans for an entirely different operation. Washington had discovered that the raw material it proposed to work up into butadiene would not be available. In due course a new set of plans was passed, but the company was ordered to build at another location. Amid negotiations for a second plant-site, permission was received to return to its original land, which in the meantime had been leased to another firm doing war work.

Lack of a single, technically informed, final authority inevitably involved our synthetic rubber program in cross-purposes. It has created conflicts, technical disputes, selfish quarrels, political squabbles. Even when technical experts have rendered professional opinions, decisions based on them have been appealed to the Administration, to Congress, to the general public through press and radio.

In Washington, William Jean had been able to get nowhere in his efforts to secure materials and equipment for his rubber-extending process until he met a member of the War Production Board's Planning Committee who happens to be a brother-in-law of President Blumberg of Universal Pictures. The energetic Jean, a tall, slender, sharp-featured man who has made money as a building-contractor and became enamored of chemical processes, had earlier dabbled with an alcohol motor fuel. Lately he has taken up this idea of stretching our dwindling rubber stocks by an extender which might be used as reclaimed rubber is employed or as naftonen, byproduct recovered from the acid sludge of oil refineries, is used to plasticize and extend bunas and even latex.

A synopsis of this proposed process and samples produced in laboratory trials had been submitted to the Rub-

ber Administration and passed upon by two competent
rubber chemists, one in the Bureau of Standards, the other
a well-known rubber consultant. Their verdict was that
neither process nor product was sufficiently promising to
warrant Government aid in development. Jean, however,
convinced the Planning Committee that he had something
and by long distance Blumberg was sold the idea, half patriotism and half publicity, of putting Universal facilities
at his disposal.

Jean set up his specifications and within twenty-four
hours his pilot plant appeared on the old location of *The
Boys from Syracuse*. The building was an open-sided shed.
Wooden vats with metal linings and stirrers were made on
the spot. The steel rollers — only the property boss knows
where they came from — needed steam, so a locomotive
was trundled alongside for a power plant. Some valves
were wooden dummies and part of the first batch was lost
before the idea was conveyed that this was to be a real
plant not a property for a shot. Where but in Hollywood
can such miracles be performed?

For a second time the Rubber Administration sent a
technical expert to make a thorough examination of the
Jean process and its product, Jeanite. He found no advantages over existing methods of extending rubber by re-
claim and plasticizers. Furthermore, he discovered serious
wartime objections. To adopt the Jean process would require new plants, to produce Jeanite would consume large
quantities of certain petroleum cuts that are critical raw
materials on the chemical front today.

The enthusiastic Bill Jean was not pleased with this expert appraisal. Naturally enough, he simply refused to be-

lieve it, and being energetic and persistent he has been trying to have this report reversed, storming Washington for priorities on rubber and the other critical materials. His version of the story has got into the newspapers, and Dr. Ernst Hauser, one of the Government's experts, has been rather roughly handled by one of the radio commentators. It is possible, of course, that these rubber chemists have all made a mistake. But Dr. Hauser is not pleased to have his professional opinion tried, not by a jury of his peers — capable, disinterested rubber chemists — but in the daily press and over the air.

When we do follow Watson Davis's capital advice and call upon the technical experts to help fight this technological war, it will not help at all if we do not abide by their authoritative decisions. It will positively hurt our cause if anyone disagreeing with their opinions can smirch their professional reputation and smear their personal integrity by wisecracks and innuendoes. Already public service is fast becoming as distasteful and dangerous to our finest chemists, physicists, metallurgists, and other highly trained scientists as it has long been to many of our best, most valuable citizens — and for exactly the same reasons. This will be a heavy handicap in the uncertain, tumultuous future that lies ahead of us.

War on the chemical front is not going to end when the bugles sound "cease firing" on the battlefields. Rubber itself is a proof of this, for our rubber problem is not going to be solved by the reopening of the Pacific. Despite bungling, our production of synthetic rubber is expanding swiftly and we are fast learning the technique of its production, its compounding, its fabrication. Synthetic rubber has arrived. It is here to stay. What it is today, what it now costs, mean very little, for as certainly as day follows night its quality will be vastly improved and its price deeply cut within the next few years. It is here and it is quite ready to challenge natural rubber for one of the world's great commodity markets.

CHAPTER XIII

LAND VERSUS LABORATORY

◇◇

COMPARED with rubber and quinine, the bug-killer pyrethrum hardly seems to be a dire war necessity. Nevertheless, a little two-ounce tin can packed with body dusting powder was "must" equipment in the pack of every American soldier throughout the North African campaign. Literally millions of them were shipped overseas. They meant not only comfort, but protection also, protection against fleas that carry the deadly typhus germ. This priceless powder contains pyrethrum eked out, because of another Japanese monopoly, with "IN-930," a chemical compound developed by du Pont chemists, a new synthetic product that actually increases the killing-power of the pyrethrum in the insect powder.

Plenty of Americans who for years have fought insect pests by squirting away gallons of flyspray have never suspected that the essential ingredient of this household necessity comes from a pretty little blossom, first cousin of the painted daisies of grandmother's old-fashioned garden, nor have they dreamed that it is one of the oldest, most romantic articles of world commerce which, in late

[173

years, has been very neatly monopolized by the great Nipponese trading-companies.

Modern flysprays are essentially a decoction of dried pyrethrum flowers in kerosene, a convenient liquid adaptation of the insect powder we sprinkle on Fido and Tabby as a flea repellent. Back in the clipper-ship days this same product was known as "Dalmatian powder" — it then came from the beautiful Balkan country east of the Adriatic — and, long before, it was on sale in the little cosmetic shops that flourished in Rome during the closing century of the great empire.

The ancient and honorable trade in pyrethrum originated some fifteen hundred years ago in the Near East, where this miniature chrysanthemum is native and where a good insect-killer is always a steady seller. It is a simple business, requiring cheap, unskilled labor. The insecticidal power depends chiefly upon the pollen. Accordingly, the flowers are gathered by hand just before they open fully, are dried, baled, and shipped off to the ends of the earth. The pyrethrum plant grows happily in almost any temperate climate — I once raised quite a crop of commercial varieties in my Connecticut garden — and it is a cut-and-come-again perennial.

Pyrethrum did not escape the insatiable curiosity of the chemists, who found that its active principle is a volatile oil which they named pyrethrin. They also discovered that pyrethrin is soluble in kerosene, so that a liquid spray might replace the dry powder with advantages in efficiency and convenience.

Pyrethrum became big business — it accounts for most of our $20,000,000 worth of household insecticides — and the wide-awake Japanese became interested. Cultivation is now centered in Thailand and China, but the trade has been almost exclusively in the hands of Japanese merchants. Of course we have been as completely cut off from Far Eastern pyrethrum as from quinine and rubber.

To make matters worse, two other vegetable insecticides, which like pyrethrum are nontoxic to man, are now hard to get. Rotenone comes from Peru and cubé root from Malaya or the Dutch East Indies. There is a real need for these weapons in our dairies and for spraying fruits and vegetables.

An ultra-modern need arises in intercontinental air travel. Since the dread bubonic plague is flea-borne, clippers from Asia and Africa must be fumigated, and it costs the airlines a $1,000 fine for each flea landed. The approved method of control has been a glorified flyspray of pyrethrum dissolved in dichlorodifluoromethane which is distributed as a mist through a hair-fine tube by means of a sort of metal seltzer bottle. With similar precaution against insect disease-carriers, the Army buys enormous quantities of these insecticides to wage sanitation campaigns in kitchens, mess tents, and hospitals. The importance of pyrethrum begins to loom bigger and bigger, and an effective chemical substitute seems now to be a worthwhile research project.

Several years ago, in the Wilmington, Delaware, laboratory of the Hercules Powder Company, where the absorbing idea is to explore all chemical possibilities of rosin, turpentine, and pine oil, some terpene derivatives were found that showed promise as insecticides. J. N. Borglin, leader of the naval stores research group at the Hercules

Experiment Station, had an idea that terpene-sulphur compounds might fit into this picture. He found some promising compounds. Several were grand insect-killers. All were checked and double-checked in an elaborate series of tests.

Then began a joint offensive on insects by this wiry little chemist, whose blue eyes sparkle with pent-up enthusiasms, and a tall, slow-motion Southerner, Friar Thompson, the company's chief entomologist, who calls himself a bugologist. Joe Borglin, the chemist, and Thompson, the insecticide expert, planned the strategy of the war. The Delaware Agricultural Experiment Station tried out the new ammunitions and reported their effectiveness against the various insect enemies.

Borglin kept hooking up combinations of organic sulphur compounds with sundry terpenes. In air-conditioned cages, maintained from January to December at the best temperature and humidity, the Delaware Experiment Station bred a hardy race of flies and counted the kill per minute of the new compounds. Thompson acted as the liaison officer between the chemist's laboratory and the testing-cages, insisting all the while that the strategy of a new insecticide demanded that it must first be a superior killer, but harmless to all animals, and that it must be made from cheap, available raw materials so it may be sold in big quantities at a low price. In due time they developed D.H.S. activator, a terpene glycol ether, a capital additive to natural pyrethrum, which it stabilized and reinforced. Quite recently they have evolved Thanite, which satisfied both bugologist and chemist as an ideal insecticide.

As the chemical demands of World War II grew, however, this new synthetic insecticide, Thanite, became involved in the ramifications of the chemical front. One essential ingredient, sodium thiocyanate, became scarce and high-priced, so the switch was made to ammonium thiocyanate, a product of the Koppers coke ovens. The result was an even more active killer of the pests that are a dangerous menace.

Du Pont's IN-930 (an almost obligatory trade-name since its proper chemical name is the tongue-twisting isobutyl undecylenamide) and Hercules' Thanite are now stretching our strictly limited stocks of pyrethrum, but they are only two of a great number of highly complicated organic chemical compounds that have been found to possess the desirable, paradoxical properties of being fatal to insects yet harmless to both plants and warm-blooded animals. Some of these come from coal-tar and others, such as Shell's Crystox, are derivatives of petroleum, hence the basis for synthesizing such useful compounds is exceedingly broad, and many improvements and new developments are certain to materialize.

One of the most interesting of these newer insecticides is phenothiazine, upon which the Bureau of Entomology of the U.S. Department of Agriculture and the Dow Chemical Company have been doing a great deal of co-operative research. It is a very versatile insecticide, for it is most effective against cattle ticks, codling-moth larvae, the tent caterpillar, the Mexican bean beetle, the tough European corn-borer, the tougher screwworm, and a swarm of others of economic importance. Maybe its most sensational accomplishment is that one part in two million kills mosquito larvae, topping the record of rotenone and holding forth a fine promise of more economical, more effective mosquito control.

New tactics have been introduced into the war on the insects by chemicals which discourage their feeding and so starve out these destructive armies, and a fascinating hunt for causes and results can be set up by these discoveries. An exhaustive study has been made to learn why the chemical tetramethylthiuram disulphide inhibits the voracious appetite of the Japanese beetle. All the usual theories have been advanced — taste, odor, irritation of various parts of the body — and tested by preparing leaves of the beetle's favorite food plants with alternate treated and untreated bands and also by dusting the beetles themselves with this chemical. Although the insects light upon the treated leaves and crawl about them in the usual manner, they refuse to eat even the untreated portions. Furthermore, if afterwards removed to fresh, untreated leaves, they still refuse to eat. In like manner, after dusting, the beetles appear to have permanently lost their appetite. It has been observed that Japanese beetles that come in contact with this chemical suffer from partial paralysis of the forelegs and mouth parts, a kind of insect delirium tremens. No doubt that herein lies the secret, but the hows and the whys are still mysterious. If this little puzzle were solved, it would reveal a great deal about this new weapon against the bugs and would doubtless suggest other chemicals and other insects that might be fought in this way.

Like a new medicine, a new insecticide must go through a long period of grueling testing — pathological and clinical as well as chemical — for its effects upon many plants and animals as well as upon scores of worms. caterpillars, bugs, beetles, flies, and others of the insect hordes. For several years the tendency has been strongly away from the poisonous insecticides, containing arsenic, copper, and lead, but until these newer developments the best non-toxic controls have been pyrethrum and rotenone. In 1940 we imported 12,591,220 pounds of pyrethrum flowers and 6,566,815 pounds of rotenone-bearing roots, which is sizable business. These imports have been drastically curtailed, and war necessity is mothering a lot of chemical youngsters that are going to throw off our dependence upon their foreign-raised, alien-controlled essentials. More natural monopolies, Japanese and others, are being broken.

Soldiers, as well as crops, need protection against insect pests, and there is no doughboy of 1918 who does not have fond memories of the good old delousing machine and the comfort it brought to the rest stations back of the front-line trenches. This effective but cumbersome method of control has been replaced by a tiny ampoule of methyl bromide and a paper bag, so handy that each man can now provide his own delousing outfit. All that he needs to do is to pack his clothes in the bag, break the thread-like neck of the glass container, dump the chemical in, and seal up the bag. The methyl bromide — used in peace to fumigate grain elevators — does the rest.

Another adaptation of the sound idea that prevention is better than cure has instigated researches to find chemicals more effective than the citronella and pennyroyal and good old bear's grease long used as insect repellents. One of the most effective is dimethyl phthalate. It is so effective that even the mosquito will not bite a skin treated with this oily substance, and according to reports from the North

African campaign this discovery may even prove to be a valuable aid in the war against malaria.

Long centuries older than the trade in insect flowers is the trade in spices, and while spices may not be the prime necessity they were in the days when highly seasoned gravy was a substitute for a refrigerator, nevertheless a big slice of our life would become dull and tasteless were we cut off completely from all condiments.

Black pepper and cinnamon — the bread-and-butter and the cake of the spice trade — come from those Spice Islands that Columbus sought when he reached the Caribbean and thought he had found a short route to the fabulous Indies. Pepper is now widely grown throughout many tropic lands, but the world headquarters for true cinnamon is still Ceylon, and its more pungent relative, cassia, which is largely used in the United States, comes almost exclusively from Indo-China and the Netherlands Indies. Since January 1941 there have been few importations, almost none, and we are short of cinnamon.

War in the Pacific was plain notice of such a famine and the price of cinnamon in the wholesale market leaped up from 20¢ to about 85¢ a pound. It was then checked by a ceiling price of 66¢. The "small box" price of ground cinnamon was 35¢ a pound prewar — usually bought by the housewife in a three-ounce package for 10¢ — and it also has been set under a ceiling of $1 a pound, which means the familiar spice box of the grocery trade now retails for 35¢. But there is no cinnamon famine and, thanks to an acceptable artificial cinnamon, there will be none.

With all sorts of condiment shortages threatening, Norman Dillingham, active·head of the oldest spice-grinding firm in the United States, went straight to one of the country's few recognized authorities on the chemistry of tastes and smells, Ernest C. Crocker of the consulting staff of Arthur D. Little, Inc. They agreed that synthetic cinnamon was the one best research bet.

By a curious coincidence, in 1834, the very year that David and Levi Slade began grinding spices in the century-old family mill at Chelsea, Massachusetts, two French chemists, Dumas and Péligot, isolated from cinnamon oil its active flavoring-principle, cinnamic aldehyde. This is a light, oily substance of yellowish tinge with the imposing chemical formula, $C_6H_5 \cdot CH \colon CH \cdot CHO$. It can be prepared synthetically by the action of caustic soda on a mixture of benzaldehyde and acetaldehyde. But cinnamic aldehyde is not the sole flavoring-element in the dried bark of the Ceylon cinnamon tree, and Ernest Crocker, co-operating with the D. & L. Slade Company and Little chemists, concocted a formula that so closely simulates the smell and taste of the natural spice that even the experts are deceived. Fixatives had also to be found and a suitable carrying-agent, which turned out to be ground pecan shells.

Although many scents have been synthesized and are used in great quantities by the perfumers, not many flavors are produced chemically. Nevertheless, one of the greatest and most commercially important of all these synthetic aromatic chemicals is vanillin, a test-tube product that, like cinnamic aldehyde, is the exact chemical duplicate of the flavoring-principle of the natural product.

Just before this war we produced 454,948 pounds of vanillin, which in these days of big figures seem few

enough. They represent, however, the equivalent flavoring
of 90,000,000 pounds of beans, or nearly a hundred times
the quantity of the fragrant pods of the vanilla vine that
we imported from Mexico, Central America, and the
French island of Madagascar, all added together.

It is a good time to pause and give thought to what
those remarkable figures mean. In the brave new world
we are all striving to achieve after the war is won, the
battle of land and laboratory is certain to be important.
Already it is plain that many of the most active and vocal
of our plan-makers cherish some appallingly erroneous notions about the roles of synthetic and natural raw materials
in our modern economics. Like poison gas this is a subject
we must view with cold realism, and the more of us who
understand the chemical background of these knotty international problems, the better it will be for all of us.

Vanilla is not a contentious commodity of world commerce today. Yet its competition with vanillin displays in
detail the tactics of the battle with chemical substitutes
that rubber, silk, cotton, vegetable oils, quinine, pyrethrum,
and a score of others must face in the near future. Vanilla
makes, therefore, a cool and pleasant introduction to these
blistering rivalries in world trade tomorrow.

In 1875 de Laire in France and Tiemann in Germany
patented within a few weeks of each other two quite different processes for the chemical preparation of vanillin,
which was shortly offered commercially at $80 a pound.
With vanilla beans selling normally at about $2.50 a pound
that seems ridiculous. But a pound of vanillin, the active
flavoring-principle, can be extracted only from 175 pounds
of grade A beans. In other words, a pound of natural vanil-

lin in beans costs normally about $450. Its chemical duplicate, synthetic vanillin, at $80 was after all a pretty good
buy.

Something of this sort happens whenever a new synthetic appears in competition with an old natural material.
The newcomer runs plumb into the stiff-necked, conservative inertia of the vast majority of its prospective buyers,
so to get even a toehold in the market it must offer some
rather tempting inducements of price, convenience, quality, or steady supply. Commonly — but not always — the
initial advantage is a lower price.

It is well to recall that the first commercially successful
synthetic rubber, du Pont's Neoprene, was originally offered at the very time when crude rubber was selling at
its all-time low price of 3½¢ a pound. Nevertheless, Neoprene was snapped up at $1 a pound by eager rubber manufacturers because it could do things — notably withstand
the ravages of oil and gasoline — that rubber could not do.

In the half-century between 1875 and 1924 the price of
vanillin was gradually, steadily reduced from $80 to $8 a
pound. This is also a familiar phenomenon of chemical
economics, an axiom based on the facts that manufacturing experience develops cheaper raw materials, lower operating-costs, and greater yields. A mountain of chemical
price statistics substantiates this, but a couple of very recent examples will suffice. Cellophane was first sold for
$2.65 a pound in 1924; a greatly improved product sold
for 33¢ in 1940. Sulfanilamide was introduced in 1937 at
$4.94 a pound and now sells for $1. Rely upon it, each new
synthetic product is but a promise, for surely its quality
will be raised and its cost lowered.

At the time vanillin was selling at $8, in 1924, the price
of vanilla beans went soaring from $2.50 to $9. This, too,
is a familiar phenomenon in the economics of natural raw
materials. It was caused by a crop shortage. It resulted in
a logical sequence of events known only too well by agri-
culturists the world over.

Vanilla beans are the fruit of a vine belonging to the
orchid family, which comes to full bearing the third year.
If carefully pruned and cultivated, vines produce profitable crops seven to ten years, after which they must be
replaced. Hence, efficient planters plan to have young
stock coming along each season to replace wornout vines.
From its original home in Mexico — the Aztecs sipped hot
chocolate flavored with vanilla a century before Cortés
destroyed their mighty, highly civilized empire — the culture of this vine has spread through many semitropical
countries. Mexican beans still command a premium price
for their superior size and flavor, but so-called Bourbon
beans from Madagascar are an important item in the trade.

During 1924 a revolution in Mexico and hurricanes and
droughts in other growing centers presented the Madagascar planters with a corner of the available supply for the
simple reason that their crop was undamaged and their
yield normal. They ran the price up to $9. Their perfectly
natural human selfishness stimulated growers the world
over to extend their plantations.

Three years later, when all the new vines came into
bearing, the market was oversupplied and the price began
tumbling. By 1932 it had sunk to 50¢ a pound, so far below
"parity" that it no longer paid to cultivate, cut, and cure
the beans. Naturally, acres of vines were neglected. The

wicked pendulum began swinging back. Two years later there was another vanilla famine and the price advanced rapidly to $3.50. It is worth noting that ten years before, under similar market conditions, the price had reached $9. During that decade a great deal had happened to vanillin.

Beans at $9 represent a cost of $1,500 a pound for their flavoring essence, vanillin, and with the identical chemical, vanillin, at $8 many industrial users — cigarette manufacturers, bakers, candy and ice cream makers — switched to the synthetic flavor. It is the proud, not empty, boast of the vanillin producers that once they sell a customer he stays everlastingly sold.

There are good reasons for this and they apply with great force to any synthetic material. One of the nastiest headaches of any manufacturer is caused by sharp fluctuations in the cost of his raw materials. They upset all his plans and raise havoc with the business. Especially if he is selling to the general public, he dare not keep moving his own selling price up and down, so he must set it high enough to afford as much margin of safety as competition will permit. Then he simply gambles with the market for his raw-material costs.

Chemically produced materials are not prey to heat or frost, to rain or drought, to plagues of insects or blights of disease. They are less apt to be disturbed by man-made risks of wars and revolutions, shipping-pools or currency juggling, by speculative buying or corners of available stocks. And never forget that the trend of chemical prices is inevitably downwards. As far back as authentic American records exist, the chemical price curve has come down, save only in wartime, down from an index number of 428

(1800) to 93 (1940) while the price of "all commodities" registered then 118 and now 112.

When the $9 price of vanilla beans encouraged greater vanilla plantations, it also stimulated a larger use of synthetic vanillin. Results in the two fields were vastly different. Greater production of the chemical lowered the price from $8 to $4.50 in 1932, the very year the natural price pendulum began swinging back. It is another chemical axiom that the more of a product you can sell, the cheaper it can be made. The beau ideal is a sufficiently big output to set up an automatically controlled, 24-hour, 365-day operation. The closer this is approached, the greater the savings in operating-costs — equipment, power, labor — the more efficient the process, and the greater the yield.

It follows, too, that the larger market attracts at once new competition and further research. In the case of vanillin recent research has discovered a new raw material. This synthetic aromatic chemical had historically been prepared from eugenol, an isolate of natural cloves, and from guaiacol, fractioned from the coal-tar intermediate phenol. For years these two processes had competed commercially. Lately a process starting with lignin, a waste product of the woodpulp industry, has been perfected by the Marathon Paper Mills of Wisconsin. Once again the price of vanillin was cut, this time to $2 a pound.

In competition with any natural material a synthetic has still another advantage, one that is weighty indeed in the streamlined, assembly-belt methods of modern mass production. Variation is the first law of nature. Vanilla beans from Mexico and Madagascar are so different that they are identified as distinct trade grades. From country to country, even from plantation to plantation, always from season to season in a given locality, the quantity and quality of the flavoring essence varies. It is also affected by age, by care, by curing. Accordingly, the preparation of vanilla extract, by percolating with alcohol, is an art. Each batch must be tested by taste and blended to an arbitrary, inexact standard. But every ounce of vanillin is always the same. Whether it is made in St. Louis, Missouri; Wilmington, Delaware; or Delawanna, New Jersey, from cloves, coal-tar, or wood, each ounce will invariably produce the identical flavoring-effect tomorrow or next month. A recipe or a formula can be indefinitely and exactly repeated.

Furthermore, synthetic products can frequently be tailor-made to meet specific requirements. Vanillin is a definite chemical compound used only for flavoring, but the competition of the low-cost lignin process is being met by the older manufacturers with ethylvanillin, a chemical of the same series but four times as strong in flavor. Rayon can be deliberately varied as to the fineness of the filament, which may also be formed round or flat or curved, while it may be spun in a continuous length or cut into staples of any length desired. No natural fiber displays such versatility. Materials like synthetic resins present almost infinite combinations and permutations of chemical and physical properties.

Vanilla versus vanillin is a thoroughly typical story of competition between natural and synthetic products. With minor variations it is the story of indigo and madder dyes, of camphor, musk, wintergreen, attar of roses, wood alco-

hol, citric acid, and of a host of others. The plot of that
story is now as obvious to us all as the tactics of the blitzkrieg, its climax as inevitable as that of a Greek classical
tragedy.

Once a new synthetic gets but a toehold in the market,
it is not to be dislodged, and the war has flung wide open
the door of this opportunity to many chemically made materials. We have learned bitter lessons in the folly of dependence upon foreign sources of essential raw materials,
and it will be a grievous mistake if we so misread the story
of land versus laboratory that we confuse sensible national
self-sufficiency with unreasoning isolationism.

From such a confusion arises the proposal that it would
be a good-neighborly act for us to repatriate the rubber
tree in South American plantations. On the contrary, considered realistically from the chemical point of view, such
a gesture can only raise false hopes destined to be shattered.

Technically, synthetic rubber is no longer an experiment. Economically, it now has its opportunity. As a matter of fact, natural rubber is exceedingly vulnerable to
attack. It has a villainous reputation for price instability.
Its wild swing from $3\frac{1}{2}\mathcal{C}$ to $3.10 is a record touched by no
other important industrial raw material. Despite its in-
valuable, unique combination of properties — stretch and
bounce, indifference to moisture and electricity — it has
many faults. It is seriously and permanently damaged by
air, heat, sunlight, oil, gasoline, and many chemicals. It
requires elaborate, expensive processing to fit it for the
tasks we want it to do. No material is ideal for all the purposes, but rubber falls far short of being satisfactory. So

true is this that an important rubber industrialist once exclaimed: "Rubber is a headache!"

Already we have not one, but four rubberlike materials. Within a few years we shall have many. Each will have distinctive, useful properties, and those that prove out will improve in quality and become cheaper in price. We shall free ourselves from foreign dependence. Never again will rubber prices go skyrocketing. The consumption of rubberlike materials will increase and we shall use them in many new ways.

These are the plain facts in the face of which some of our Government representatives have promised our South American neighbors not only to help them finance rubber plantations, but also to scrap our own synthetic rubber plants after the war. That promise in the Rio de Janeiro Agreement is couched in highly diplomatic language: "That the nations of the Americas stimulate the development of the basic production of each of them, avoiding in so far as possible the establishment or expansion of production of substitute or synthetic commodities which is economically artificial and might displace the consumption of natural products available in other American nations, there being excepted only those industries which are indispensable for national defense, provided that such defense needs cannot be effectively met with natural products."

There are many weasel words in that promise, but if it was not made in good faith why have we spent millions encouraging South American rubber projects which from a defense point of view do not make sense? They would still be a foreign source of supply, and our necessary rationing of coffee in this war reveals that even the intra-hemisphere trade lines can be cut.

Time also is of the essence of this problem. Charles Morrow Wilson, whose *Trees and Test Tubes* is an authoritative appeal for rubber grown in the Americas, assures us that within fifteen years Brazil could send us 400,000 tons of plantation rubber, less than a third of our present consumption. The most conservative of the rubber experts assure us that within fifteen years we shall have a synthetic tire that will be nonskid, punctureproof, good for 100,000 miles, and cheaper than 1939 prices. The simon-pure enthusiasts talk of rubberlike materials so cheap and plentiful that they will be smeared over our city streets and highways to give us a noiseless, nonslip, shock-absorbing surface.

Such prophecy may be foolhardy, but it is not more rash than an attempt to thwart by treaty or control by law the march of progress. And the story of the synthetics is a modern saga of scientific progress that means more goods, cheaper goods, better goods, for all the people.

Instead of holding forth false hopes to our neighbors we should help them develop their resources realistically. Nobody dreams that synthetic elastomers will replace crude rubber entirely. But they may curtail its market and they will certainly force its price down, so that there will have to be serious readjustments in the economy of the rubber-producing lands. It will not help to subsidize new rubber plantations. Maybe there is a hint in the story of indigo versus indigotin: when the coal-tar dye literally ruined the vast indigo plantations of India those same acres were planted in millet, which has helped to reduce the recurring threat of the great Indian famines. Food is still our first essential, and every acre taken from growing industrial raw materials becomes thus a promise of greater food supply.

CHAPTER XIV

THE PLASTICS VICTORY

◇◇

A REGULATION U.S. Army bugle weighs 20 ounces. For the past two centuries it has been made of brass, the finest virgin brass, an alloy three-fourths of which is copper, and today copper is a critical metal. What with waste and scrap, it takes one and one-half pounds of precious copper to make an Army bugle, and the Quartermaster Corps was figuring on 200,000 bugles!

That is why, one day in May 1942, Major E. L. Hobson at Headquarters in Washington put in long-distance calls to a number of leading plastic-molders and asked: "Can you make an Army bugle out of plastics?"

Some hemmed and others hawed. A few said they would try, but most were certain it could not be done. At last he called: "Chicago, Mills Plastic Products, Haymarket 2523," and like a shot came back the bland reply: "Why, certainly."

Major Hobson was skeptical and did not hesitate to say so.

"Of course, that's a fast answer," the words purred in his ear, "but I don't make foolish promises."

"I know — of course not, but —"

192]

"If you want a bugle, we can make it for you." The soft voice had suddenly acquired a sharp edge.

It is said that Elmer Mills believes that plastics can do almost anything and sometimes do it better than the traditional materials. In this case he was not taking great chances, for he had already molded millions of little toy bugles that added considerably to the din of last Christmas morning. He is a short man with an admittedly short temper and he has a constitutional objection to being told that something cannot be done — in plastics. His hobby is finding unique uses for plastics and making them work.

A fortnight later Elmer Mills called Major Hobson. "We've got your bugle," he said.

"Splendid! Ship it down to me for testing, and if it proves out, we'll send for you in a couple of weeks and we can talk it over."

"Sorry, but I've got the only plastic bugle on earth and I'm not shipping it anywhere, not even to you in Washington. I'll bring it down. We'll be in your office day after tomorrow at nine o'clock, and be sure to have all your gang on hand to test it right then and there, because we are terrifically busy and I can't leave that model with you."

That unique model which Mills guarded like a sacred relic was not simply plucked out of the air. After Major Hobson's request, he had gone straight to M. H. Berlin, president of the Chicago Musical Instrument Company, for whom he had previously molded the toy trumpets. They called in a man as unique in his way as the bugle he produced. Frank Aman was born in Hungary of a family which for a century and a half has produced generation after generation of musical-instrument makers. At eleven he was apprenticed to a famous one, his own uncle, Ludwig Windisch. At twenty-three Aman was foreman in the Hohner woodwind factory in Hamburg. In 1907 he came to this country and since has conducted a musical-instrument repair shop, greater in fame than in size, and on occasion turned out a flute or some other instrument to special order. This skilled genius produced that model bugle, which, if one is technically minded in musical matters, is a conical-bore tube, without side openings, relying for its scale on the harmonic series obtained by overblowing. In everyday words, the notes a bugle produces depend upon the length, the bore, and the shape of the tube. Only five notes are actually required to blow the Army's forty-one calls. A bugle's tonal and carrying qualities depend largely upon the material and in these respects nothing had ever equaled brass.

When Elmer Mills and M. H. Berlin arrived at the Quartermaster Corps headquarters with the plastic bugle they were met by a formidable jury of experts. The instrument was stood up, bell down, on Major Hobson's desk and eyed critically.

"No use looking at it," said Major Hobson. "Let's hear it."

He nodded to a big soldier with the insignia of a sergeant musician and who was, in fact, the solo cornetist of the U.S. Army Band, reputed to be the best bugler in Washington. He picked up the plastic bugle and almost lost his balance backwards. He was expecting to lift nearly a pound. He had picked up eight ounces.

"Holy smoke!" he exploded. "Do you expect me to blow this?"

"Try taps," somebody suggested.

"That's it," cut in Mills quickly, "taps for brass, reveille for plastics."

Everybody laughed and then the bugler sounded taps. He himself was the most astonished man in that astonished group. Not only did this feather-weight thing blow; it blew so easily, the notes were so clear, the tone so perfect. He stared at the instrument as if it were some curious, be-witched charm, and then he suddenly thought that, after all, taps is a slow call, easy to blow. He lifted it to his lips and sounded reveille, followed immediately by boots and saddles. It took the quick notes and the trills perfectly, and it did not choke up.

The whole party adjourned outdoors for a trial in the open. Then they scattered half a mile to judge the carry-ing ability of the plastic bugle against a selected one of brass, and because the signs got mixed up nobody could agree as to which was the better. Next they went over to the War College and the plastic-versus-brass contest was staged before other experts. At this point Captain Darcy, commanding officer of the U.S. Army Band, came out flatly with his opinion that the plastic bugle's tonal quality was positively superior to that of the regular issue instrument.

After lunch the plastic model was given a fourth-degree examination by the QMC's Technical Committee, from which Mills and Berlin were politely excluded. It must have been a grueling trial, for among other things these Army perfectionists measured the frequency of each note on the delicate recording stroboscope and they hurled the plastic bugle across the room against the wall. By 4:30 that afternoon — which is reputed to be the all-time record for

swift approval in Washington — Mills had instructions to
go ahead.

Back in Chicago the Mills Corporation chief engineer,
Herbert S. Ruekberg, and the vice president, Raymond
Dawson, designed the dies for the thirteen different parts
of the molded-plastic bugle. It was a job demanding ex-
quisite precision, for the dimensions of the double-looped
tubing must be exact from one end to the other, else the
tone will be off. The various parts must fit together with
scrupulous accuracy. Then a series of tests were made of
various cellulose plastic molding materials to determine
the one best fitted to this novel application, and final approval from the QMC went to Tenite II, product of the
Eastman Tennessee Corporation, the plastics subsidiary
of the Kodak Company.

First suggested as a copper-saving substitute by Major
Hobson, who has become one of the Army's plastics enthusiasts, the plastic bugle has an impressive array of firsts
scored against brass. It is lighter and it costs less. Its performance is better in tone, in volume, in ease of blowing.
An ordinary drop to the ground dents brass, but leaves the
plastic unharmed. A severe blow sends the brass bugle to
the instrument repair shop, while if it cracks the plastic
bugle the fracture can be quickly and perfectly mended
by painting the broken edges with acetone and pressing
them together tightly for a few moments. Even at six a.m.
on a January morning the plastic bugle needs no warming
up before it can be blown and it does not readily choke up.
Finally, it is fabricated in a permanent olive-drab color,
quite correct for field service and saving the bugler endless brass-polishing.

The tale of the plastic bugle has a moral. Prior to 1942 the Army could not see plastics with a telescope. That was then a fairly common eye complaint. Many of us regarded them as smart substitutes, and millions of dollars of good advertising had impressed upon us that "just as good" is either an excuse or a fraud. The attitude of the Army was that it needed the best materials in everything and it was not wasting time with makeshift stuff that was just splendid for cigarette holders and costume jewelry, but — As for plastics being necessary replacements for critically short materials — well, who then dreamed of priorities in the United States on steel and gasoline and meat?

The makers of plastic materials complained bitterly of this unjustly frivolous regard of their wares. Gadgets, indeed! They knew that synthetic plastics were revolutionary materials, quite capable of upsetting old industries and creating new businesses. But they could do little about it, save to go ahead developing new types with new characteristics and to keep on discovering fresh applications.

Ten days after Pearl Harbor the plastics industry had an electrifying shock. More than 300 representatives of the Army, Navy, Office of Production Management, and various other Government agencies attended a plastics meeting in Washington. Major C. V. Morgan of the Munitions Board set forth by word and chart the national supply, present and projected, of metals, other materials, and the different types of plastics. Dr. Gordon Kline of the Bureau of Standards discussed plastic substitutes, even substitutes for those plastics whose raw materials were themselves likely to become critical materials. Eugene Vidal explained the war uses of plastic-bonded plywoods. There was an exhibit of plastic warstuffs and a straight talk about how the nation's plastics output might be kicked up.

Such knowing, flattering attention was a bit staggering, but makers of plastic materials and plastics fabricators both hugged the opportunity and plunged wholeheartedly into war work. Within a few months Major Hobson was calling by long distance for a plastic bugle to save copper, and the Army Medical Corps, which for years refused to consider anything but rubber hospital sheets, had proved to its own satisfaction that plastic-impregnated rayon, similar to your shower curtains, is less susceptible to acids, salts, blood, perspiration; is lighter, more durable, and actually costs less. Since then applications of plastics to war purposes have multiplied till a book bigger than this would not begin to describe those that are not today military secrets.

Even in their pride plastics zealots seldom agree. In trying to pick their own outstanding war contribution they do have a bewildering array to choose from, all the way from the tiny spiral springs in the mechanism of certain bombs to the gigantic forms for shaping plywood airplane fuselages which are the largest objects ever molded of plastic materials. A historic triumph was the successful molding of a mortar shell fuse in the spring of 1942, for it led the way to many plastics developments in artillery ammunition. The liner of the Army helmet, the Army canteen, and the face parts of the Army gas mask, plastics all, each presented its own fresh technical problems. They are without doubt the three that Johnny Doughboy will remember best.

Being thoroughly realistic in their attitude, the men of

PLASTIC SCABBARD AND STEERING WHEEL.

the plastics industry like to talk about the savings of pounds of metals, of man-hours of labor, of dollars and cents that they have contributed to the war effort. It is their favorite sales argument even for war contracts which are proverbially impervious to cost considerations. All the statistics will never be compiled, but the one set of figures collected for one plastics molder for one year's war work is said by Charles Breskin, the industry-spirited publisher of the business magazine *Modern Plastics,* to be a typical sample. In twelve months the Cruver Manufacturing Company saved the Government 1,459,000 pounds of critical metals (chiefly brass, copper, steel, and aluminum), more than 250,000 man-hours in fabricating time, and $834,000. That is a nice contribution to remember when you draw your next income-tax check.

Plastics contributions to aviation have been almost innumerable. Many of them are critically important. The development of the transparent noses, gun turrets, and navigation blisters is doubly interesting, since it reveals at once how plastics meet vital needs and how they may be modified to do a new job better. For this particular job glass was simply out. Even were it not for the technical difficulties of curving sheet glass, its extreme brittleness was a dangerous drawback not to be wholly overcome in a combat plane by safety glass. A clear, transparent plastic was unanimously nominated. Aloft in the stratosphere the first one used developed two unexpected faults. Its optical properties are so superior to those of ordinary window glass that it transmits freely the actinic rays of the sun and the men inside are painfully sunburned. In the subzero atmosphere it became more brittle than glass, so that the tap of a fingernail shattered it to fragments. The plastics people pulled one of their neatest tricks out of the bag when they stuck together three paper-thin sheets of different plastics and solved all the problems.

These high-flying plastic "greenhouses" are spectacular, but hidden among the innards of engines and electrical systems plastics not only replace metals and rubber to save weight, but also to meet the rigorous unaccustomed temperatures and pressures of stratosphere flying where familiar materials failed.

Comparisons are odious, and useless, and I should divide the honors for the plastics' most valuable contribution to victory between their widely advertised plastic-bonded plywoods and their little-heralded replacements of rubber. Plywood planes and landing-boats will play a bigger and bigger part as the war goes on, and for the future everything from plywood automobiles and freight cars to plywood bathtubs and carpet sweepers has been cheerfully forecast. In the rubber-conservation program the polyvinyl resins and ethyl cellulose by special treatment with vegetable oils have all had a share, and their applications run the gamut from hospital sheeting to cushions for gun mounts. Assuming that the plastics have arrived, the synthetic rubberlike materials seem destined to be the next big development in our brilliant chemical future.

In the thick of war we have developed a new plastic; new, that is, to big commercial output. Literally thousands of rare chemicals have for many years been prepared and sold by the Eastman Kodak Company. These are one of this corporation's great contributions to chemical progress, a responsible source of unusual items often of crucial value in research. One of these rare chemicals was melamine, and in 1937 you might have bought a few grams at the snug price of $40 a pound. Kodak probably lost money on the sale, for this department of the business has never been run with an eye on the ledger. Today you can buy a carload of a melamine plastic for less than 40¢ a pound. That is, you can if you have a high priority, for this new plastic is the one from which the Army's new buttons and the Navy's new tableware are molded, and it has other war uses, some of which are vital secrets.

Because melamine is prepared from dicyanamide the American Cyanamid Company was logically interested in exploring its chemical possibilities, and in its laboratory at Stamford, Connecticut, Palmer Griffith found that it reacted with formaldehyde to form a resin. This is a similar reaction to that of formaldehyde and phenol (Bakelite, Durez, Resinox, and Durite) as well as formaldehyde and urea (Plaskon and Beetle), and this new material seemed promising. Three small ashtrays were molded and a little sample of lacquer prepared from it. Both plastic and lacquer had interesting, superior qualities worth investigating. First requisite was a commercial process for melamine itself, and literally hundreds of reactions were tried and failed before Louis Christmann and Dave Jayne evolved one that at least gave workable quantities for further research. But this was still far from a commercial-scale operation.

Convinced that these reactions would go more smoothly and that the yields would increase if carried on under pressure in the presence of ammonia gas, Robert Swain, direc-

tor of research at Stamford, moved bag and baggage to
Niagara Falls with permission to work with suitable equipment in the pilot plant of the Hooker Electrochemical
Company. This idea proved feasible and back in Stamford
a stainless-steel autoclave was adapted for another trial.
A larger steel autoclave was available at the plant of Cyanamid's subsidiary, Calco, and their Victor King and Carl
Mensing were called into collaboration. At Stamford there
was no trouble with corrosion of the stainless-steel autoclave, but there was no reason to suspect that the chemicals in this reaction would attack plain steel. However, at
Calco the high yields of melamine were accompanied by
almost equally good yields of iron dissolved from the
equipment by corrosion. Accordingly, a new set of stainless-steel equipment had to be ordered. After several
weeks' continuous run in the testing laboratory, a commercial operation was set up at the Calco plant.

All hands worked two days and nights setting up
the apparatus, checking the pressure-temperature curves,
charging the autoclave for the momentous first run. Everything seemed to be going well and at last the great moment came, climax of nearly two years' work. Two men
stood by with shovels to aid in discharging the first big
batch of melamine. The manhole of the stainless-steel
filter was thrown open and all crowded about for the first
glimpse. The filter was empty.

Where had the precious crystals gone? Through the
filter with the mother-liquor perhaps — but when samples
were evaporated there was still no melamine. Finally some-
one peered through the peephole of the converter and

there it was, completely solidified in the autoclave. It took two days to dig it out.

"We've got a lot of high-class chemical talent standing around," said Joe Paden bitterly, "but what we really need is a couple of good husky coal miners."

In time they licked the process into shape and rare melamine became an industrial chemical. Telling its story now is rather like reporting a baseball game at the end of the fifth inning, for as Reginald Banks, Cyanamid's vice president charged with melamine's marketing, says, "We're cheerful because the score is in our favor, but there are lots of plays still to make and there'll be errors as well as hits."

Melamine plastics are not the only new ones. In a small office, tucked behind a conference room, beyond a double set of locked doors, I have seen three that, as my guide to this sanctum of research progress said, "look likely." One of them, particularly so; something quite new in its raw materials and its properties. It would seem to be the answer to the engineer's prayer for a noiseless, self-lubricating gear.

But today the plastics industry is all out for victory, seeking new ways to help the war effort, proving time and again that its substitute materials do many things better than the natural materials they replace. A conference was held at the Warwick Hotel in Philadelphia last winter to consider plastics as aircraft materials on their own merits. After the chairman had outlined the objectives, he added that in the air even the slightest superiority is important and he cited instances of how the Spitfires bested the Mes-

serschmitts in the Battle of Britain. Then up spoke a War
Production Board man:

"I'm afraid, gentlemen, we are wasting our time. Even
if you find places where plastics are superior, they are fast
becoming critical materials. Frankly, we don't know where
the chemicals to make more plastics are coming from."

Silence fell like a pall, then a sharp voice blurted out:
"That's the silliest statement I ever heard!" and Charlie
Romieux, sales manager of Cyanamid plastics, sprang to
his feet. "Don't you believe a word of it," he pleaded earnestly with the assembled experts.

Then, as suddenly as he had exploded, he relaxed and a
cheerful smile banished his angry frown. "You just tell us
what you want; we'll get it for you some way by hook or
crook."

CHAPTER XV

LIQUID POWER

◇◇◇

NOBODY dissented when, three years ago, Graham Edgar said: "No single raw material appears to be so vital to the prosecution of modern war as petroleum."

Head of the research department of the Ethyl Corporation, he is one of our top-flight authorities on gasoline, and when he speaks on this subject, which is not often, he knows what he is talking about. But after that initial agreement, almost everybody, professionals and laymen alike, guessed wrong.

When the Nazi blitzkrieg was launched against Poland, it was generally believed that this wonderful military machine would soon stall for lack of petroleum. Too simple arithmetic could add up all German-controlled oil resources to a pitiful total and some very wishful miscalculations were made of German ability to produce synthetic fuels. The output and reserves of the Rumanian fields were hopefully discounted.

The British, relying as they habitually do on their Navy, were quite confident that the blockade of liquid fuel and lubricants would be a stranglehold on the throttle of the Nazi mechanized army. It was the same plan that miscarried in the last war. Then the expected military paralysis from lack of Chilean nitrates was broken by Fritz Haber's air-nitrogen process. Not till after the Battle of Britain did it become clear that whatever crippling shortages beleaguered Germany might suffer, lack of gasoline was not to be the first.

Nevertheless, as in the case of nitrogen in World War I, nobody — not excepting the Nazi campaign planners themselves — realized how enormous the war demand for petroleum products was to be. The attack upon Russia, a brazen move to assure petroleum supplies, was prompted by the threatened lack of this vital fluid. Someday the reality of this threat may be dated from the spring of 1943, when the Allies first won air supremacy.

We were not more astute in judging petroleum requirements. Submarine sinkings of tankers, not only on the Atlantic seaboard, but also at the very gates of Tunisia and Morocco, helped throw calculations out. We did not foresee, however, the needs of lend-lease or the swift development of big bombers and cargo planes which have conspired to shove our high-test fuel needs higher and ever higher. Round-the-clock demolition bombing and a cargo fleet whose minimum requirements of 100-octane gas are set at some 3,000,000 gallons a day — greater by a third than our total output of this type of gasoline in 1941 — were not in the 1939 picture when the Army and Navy drew up their gasoline schedules.

Gas rationing was a sudden, stunning blow on the point of the American jaw. To a people who would rather have the mortgage on the old homestead foreclosed than give up the family jalopy, tire rationing was shocking enough.

PONTOON BRIDGE OF PLASTIC PLYWOOD.

But a gasoline shortage — that seemed as unreasonable as a killing frost on the Fourth of July. Everybody knew that we burned up more gasoline than the rest of the world, but then everybody thought he knew that we were blessed with the most abundant petroleum supplies on earth.

In its accustomed role rubber cushioned the shock of this blow by furnishing an official excuse for doling out motor fuel, but even this did not seem very adequate to those Americans who were constrained to crawl at 35 miles per hour through veritable forests of oilwell derricks. Not till the 1,000-ton bombings and the snapping of the Big Inch pipeline by the raging Arkansas River did the little gas coupons make sense to most Americans.

So radically have we revised our thinking, however, that when Petroleum Administrator Ickes solemnly declared that after the war the United States would be an importer, no longer an exporter, of crude oil, nobody laughed out loud. Some householders who had converted their oil furnaces to coal began to speculate cheerfully whether their foresight was quite as commendable as their patriotism.

Toluene for explosives and butadiene for rubber have for the first time made petroleum a big-tonnage chemical raw material. It is pretty plain, therefore, that crude oil has taken on new jobs, and with an eye cocked skyward at potential postwar aviation our petroleum geologists and chemists are scratching their heads as they estimate anew our future requirements and measure them against reserves. All this gives every one of us something to ponder, for we have come to a fresh, acute appreciation of liquid power.

It is nothing new for American petroleum to change

jobs. For a couple of centuries it was an unmitigated nuisance, a ne'er-do-well who interfered with salt wells and polluted streams. It went into business as a patent medicine — "Seneca Oil," "Old Indian Oil," "Rock Oil," and a score of others, each modestly commended in circus-poster language as the sovereign remedy for virtually everything from falling hair to fallen arches.

One of the medicine men, watchful Sam Kier of Pittsburgh, launched petroleum on its sensational career as an illuminant. At 50¢ a half-pint bottle he had done handsomely with Kier's Rock Oil — "none genuine without the signature of the proprietor" — but the crude oil he scooped up from shallow salt wells outran the sales made by his half-dozen traveling medicine shows. With an amazing display of wisdom he sought out one of the few competent consulting chemists in America, James Curtis Booth of Philadelphia, gave him a generous sample, and put up to him the question of new uses.

Booth distilled a portion of his sample and, by separating the different distillates as they came over at different temperatures, found that it yielded a large percentage of a clear, white oil. This smelly liquid burned with excellent lighting properties in a new-fangled type of lamp designed to burn coal-oil, another innovation obtained by sweating soft coal in a retort according to a recently invented Scotch process. Booth reported these facts to his Pittsburgh client.

Kier had a sharp eye for the main chance. Following his consultant's advice he built a little brick furnace with a 5-gallon iron pot equipped with a long neck. Here was a glorified retort such as the alchemists devised for distillation centuries ago, the same that served as the model for the little brass insignia that identify the men of our Army's Chemical Warfare Service today. It was the first petroleum still in all the world. The year was 1856.

Whale oil was getting scarce and expensive. Kerosene was a better illuminant than coal-oil. At $1 a gallon — 62½¢ wholesale — it captured the market. By the time Grant and Lee came to terms at Appomattox, it was furnishing the light in the window for even frontier homesteads in Kansas and Iowa. Our modern petroleum industry had been born.

Its first problem — and undoubtedly it will also be its last — was a shortage of raw material. In those pioneering days the supply came from seepages skimmed off ponds or scooped up from wells. On August 28, 1859, however, a lean, humorous railroad conductor, Edwin Laurencine Drake, drilling for a little group of New Haven adventurers headed by George Bissell, struck oil at 69½ feet in the wilds of western Pennsylvania. It was the first oilwell, an honest-to-goodness artesian well of crude petroleum, and it caused the first oil boom. Within four years the price of petroleum dropped from $20 a barrel to $2. That collapse was the first oil panic.

Fifteen years later another courageous and lucky oil operator drove his drill to the unheard-of depth of 400 feet and pierced the so-called third sand level of the Pennsylvania field, from which poured forth the first oil gusher. Many gushers tapping this famous stratum literally flooded the oil market, and in 1889 the price dropped to a record low of 15¢ a barrel. Naturally, another oil panic followed, but boundless supplies at low prices did a lot of things to the petroleum industry.

Our infant petroleum technology consisted of simple distillation of crude oil. Save for many refinements in apparatus, designed in the main to control the temperatures of fractional distillation more exactly, this is essentially the process now called straight-run refining. Then crude yielded roughly 75 per cent of kerosene, the chief commercial product; about 2 per cent of lubricating-oils, profitable byproducts; 10 per cent of gasoline, a bothersome waste. Electricity and the automobile have turned this situation upside down.

Until about 1910 the chemistry of petroleum was as neglected as the study of Eskimo grammar. A few highly professional chemists, chiefly college professors, had analyzed it and discovered that like coal-tar it is a mixture of hydrocarbons, from gas to pitch, all combinations of only two elements, hydrogen and carbon. In petroleum are several families or series of these hydrocarbons. The paraffins — methane, CH_4, ethane, C_2H_6, on up to pentatriacontane, $C_{35}H_{72}$, all built up regularly on the general formula of C_nH_{2n+2} — are the most numerous and abundant. The four lowest members of the group — methane to butane — are gases driven off by the application of very gentle heat. They are collected and used for fuel, propane and butane being the basis of the bottled gases Pyrofax and Philgas. Butane is a favorite starting-point for the synthesis of butadiene.

As the heat is raised, the next products to distill off are the hydrocarbons with five and six carbons, pentane and hexane. When the temperature reaches between 100 and 400 degrees F., the cut or fraction comprises ordinary, straight-run gasoline. At about 400 degrees the kerosene cut comes over, and at higher temperatures are recovered successively the light and heavy oil fractions. These last yield, respectively, lubricating-oils and waxes. At the end a tarlike residue is left in the still. This may be used as asphalt, or still further heated to produce a fine-grained, porous coke employed in delicate metallurgical operations and in the manufacture of electrical carbon for electrodes.

While the paraffin series furnishes most of the components of petroleum, it is not the sole hydrocarbon family at home in this complex material. The hydrocarbons of petroleum series generally have a chainlike, open-end molecular structure. The commoner hydrocarbons found in coal-tar, on the other hand, have a closed, ringlike structure, most of them of the famous benzene ring, the six-sided figure which frames the crossed retorts in the Chemical Warfare insigne, similar to the design at the top of the back of this book's cover.

The chemist's ability to hook side or branch chains onto the open-chain molecules and to twist them about into ring structures makes crude petroleum an exceedingly versatile raw material for chemical synthesis. Its possibilities are far greater than coal-tar, from which, during the past seventy-five years, hundreds of thousands of new organic compounds — dyes, medicines, perfumes, flavors, explosives, whatnot — have been prepared. As a hint of similar possibilities latent in the petroleum hydrocarbons, it has been mathematically calculated that eicosane of the paraffin series, with the formula $C_{19}H_{40}$, has 366,319 possible isomers; that is, it is theoretically possible to rearrange the 19 carbon and 40 hydrogen atoms in this substance to make this astonishing total of different, distinct compounds.

The possibilities of synthesis from petroleum are further increased by the fact that some crudes already contain

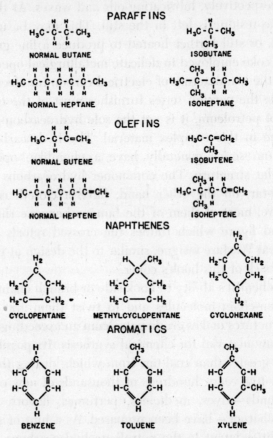

Typical hydrocarbon groups found in gasoline. (From Graham Edgar, *Gasoline, Past, Present, and Future*)

hydrocarbons of two different ring series, the naphthene and the benzene. One does not need to be much of an organic chemist to see from the graphic table of various typical hydrocarbons of gasoline that the potentialities of chemical juggling here are almost infinite.

Petroleum from different fields differs greatly in the kind and proportion of the hydrocarbons it contains. In colors it runs from amber to cherry-red, from light green to black; in odors, from sickeningly sweet to skunklike. Pennsylvania oil is famous for the high quality of its lubricants. Some oils are contaminated with sulphur, which gives them an evil smell. California oil contains an exceptionally large percentage of ring-structure or cyclic hydrocarbons. A very approximate general average content of run-o'-well American petroleums analyzes somewhat like this: gases, 4 per cent; naphthas and gasoline, 10 to 40 per cent; kerosene, 10 to 20 per cent; middle-fraction gas oils, 20 to 40 per cent; paraffin waxes, 0 to 5 per cent; asphalt, all the way up to 40 per cent.

About the time the horseless carriage was becoming an automobile, say 1910, nature's distribution of the hydrocarbons in American crude oils began to seem most inconsiderate. The petroleum refiners had gone out of the illuminating into the fuel business, gasoline had replaced kerosene as their bread-and-butter product. The half-million sputtering, steaming cars that jolted over the rutty roads that year were to double every twelvemonth during the next decade. The demand for "gas" was zooming.

At first the refiners feared they would be swamped in a flood of naphtha, kerosene, lubricating-oils, wax, and pitch. Then they began to worry that someday they would run out of petroleum if motorists continued to burn up 25 per cent of their crude and forced them virtually to discard the other three-fourths.

To squirm out of this untenable position refiners began stripping gasoline from the natural gas which they had previously let blow or at best burned as fuel under their own stills. By 1920 they were getting 9,000,000 barrels of this so-called natural gasoline. Now they recover more than 60,000,000 barrels. This helped some, as the old gentleman said when asked if coffee did not keep him awake. It did not, however, solve the problem. Some way must be found either of building up the lower carbon combinations or of breaking down the higher ones into the 6-to-10 carbon group that can be burned in the internal-combustion engine. This was clearly a chemical problem capable only of a chemical solution.

In the Gay Nineties, when the oil business was a booming bonanza, only a very few, very far-sighted petroleum refiners understood these problems or suspected that there might be a good deal of chemistry involved in distilling a lot of hydrocarbons. One of these was John D. Rockefeller. He tried to make a chemical alliance with his Cleveland neighbor, Eugene Grasselli, and it is interesting to speculate what might have happened to the American petroleum industry if the chemical experience and technical imagination of the Grasselli Chemical Company had at that early date been merged with the petroleum knowledge and organizing ability of the old Standard Oil Company — but the deal was never put through. Rockefeller persisted in his quaint chemical notions and went to the revolutionary extreme of putting chemists in his refineries.

One of the bright young men he hired was a big, quiet, good-looking chap, William M. Burton, a Clevelander, with a B.A. degree from Western Reserve and a Ph.D.

from Johns Hopkins. At the Whiting, Indiana, refinery he
began trying to coax more gasoline out of mid-continent
crude oil. In 1912 he put into operation the first large-scale
commercial cracking-unit, a heat process by which the
higher H-C combinations can be broken down into the
hydrocarbons of the gasoline fraction. Burton was later
awarded two of the choicest honors that can come to an
American chemist, the Perkin and the Willard Gibbs med-
als, and he climaxed his career with the presidency of the
Standard Oil Company of Indiana, the first technical man
to head a great petroleum enterprise.

He deserved all that he won. Cracking now saves millions of barrels of crude oil a year. It has doubled the gasoline output of our petroleum.

Burton did not originate the idea of cracking — he made
it a practical operation — and his process has since been
much improved. To heat-cracking has been added cracking by catalytic means, that is, by chemicals which induce
the splitting of the big molecules.

Other ways of increasing the proportion of suitable motor fuels have come into common practice. Working from
the other end, polymerization by linking molecules together builds up simpler hydrocarbons into those within
the gasoline cut. Hydrogenation, or the addition of a hydrogen atom, and alkylation, in which a hydrocarbon group
is put into a molecule in place of a hydrogen atom thus
forming a side-chain to a ring structure, are both more recent developments. The chart on the next page shows even
one who knows little chemistry the ideas involved in these
various methods of increasing the gasoline.

Petroleum refining is now deeply involved in chemis-

try. It has ceased to be a simple distillation operation and
become a particularized branch of organic chemical man-

CRACKING

$$C_{16}H_{34} \longrightarrow C_8H_{18} + C_8H_{16}$$
CETANE   OCTANE   OCTENE

ISOMERIZATION

$$H_3C-\overset{\overset{H}{|}}{\underset{\underset{H}{|}}{C}}-\overset{\overset{H}{|}}{\underset{\underset{H}{|}}{C}}-CH_3 \longrightarrow H_3C-\overset{\overset{H}{|}}{\underset{\underset{CH_3}{|}}{C}}-CH_3$$
NORMAL BUTANE   ISOBUTANE

CYCLIZATION

$$H_3C-\overset{\overset{H}{|}}{\underset{\underset{H}{|}}{C}}-\overset{\overset{H}{|}}{\underset{\underset{H}{|}}{C}}-\overset{\overset{H}{|}}{\underset{\underset{H}{|}}{C}}-\overset{\overset{H}{|}}{\underset{\underset{H}{|}}{C}}-\overset{\overset{H}{|}}{\underset{\underset{H}{|}}{C}}-CH_3 \longrightarrow \quad + 3H_2$$
NORMAL HEPTANE   TOLUENE

POLYMERIZATION

$$H_3C-\underset{\underset{CH_3}{|}}{C}=CH_2 + H_3C-\underset{\underset{CH_3}{|}}{C}=CH_2 \longrightarrow H_3C-\overset{\overset{CH_3}{|}}{\underset{\underset{CH_3}{|}}{C}}-\overset{\overset{H}{|}}{\underset{\underset{H}{|}}{C}}-C=CH_2$$
ISOBUTENE   ISOBUTENE   ISOOCTENE

HYDROGENATION

$$H_3C-\overset{\overset{CH_3}{|}}{\underset{\underset{CH_3}{|}}{C}}-\overset{\overset{H}{|}}{\underset{\underset{H}{|}}{C}}-C=CH_2 + H_2 \longrightarrow H_3C-\overset{\overset{CH_3}{|}}{\underset{\underset{CH_3}{|}}{C}}-\overset{\overset{H}{|}}{\underset{\underset{H}{|}}{C}}-\overset{\overset{H}{|}}{\underset{\underset{H}{|}}{C}}-CH_3$$
ISOOCTENE   ISOOCTANE

ALKYLATION

$$H_3C-\overset{\overset{H}{|}}{\underset{\underset{CH_3}{|}}{C}}-CH_3 + H_2C=CH_2 \longrightarrow H_3C-\overset{\overset{CH_3}{|}}{\underset{\underset{CH_3}{|}}{C}}-\overset{\overset{H}{|}}{\underset{\underset{H}{|}}{C}}-CH_3$$
ISOBUTANE   ETHYLENE   NEOHEXANE

Typical chemical reactions in modern gasoline refining. (From Graham Edgar, *Gasoline, Past, Present,*
and Future, 1942.)

ufacturing. Our gasoline is in a very true sense synthetic,
a man-made chemical combination. Only within the past
ten years, however, has anybody been concerned with the

chemical properties of gasoline. This attention has been richly rewarded.

It began with a realization by petroleum chemists that the kind of molecules in gasoline has a bearing on its tendency to knock and an appreciation by automotive engineers that knocking sets definite limits to the compression ratio and charge density of the internal combustion engine. The noisy ping-ping and accompanying heating of the engine, audible and visible signs of this abnormal type of combustion, are no longer to be tolerated as a necessary evil. They are warnings of a stumbling-block in the path to more powerful, more economical engines. Higher standards for airplane engine efficiency emphasized the knock danger signal.

Characteristically, chemists began by separating out all the different hydrocarbons in the gasoline fraction and examining their knocking properties in standardized testing-engines. They were confronted with unexpected, disconcerting facts. But first they must have a reliable yardstick to measure knocking.

Of all the pure hydrocarbons they had tested for knocking, they chose the best and the worst. The best was iso-octane, C_8H_{18}; the worst, heptane, C_7H_{16}. The first they designated as 100, the latter, zero. A gasoline is tested by comparing its knock against a mixture of these two pure hydrocarbons, and the percentage of octane in the comparison mixture that equals that of tested gas determines its octane number. If, for example, a gasoline behaves like a mixture of three parts of iso-octane and one part of heptane, it is rated a 75-octane gas. The 100-octane gas has as good anti-knock properties as pure iso-octane.

Wise old Aristotle warned that until we can measure a thing in numbers we know really nothing at all about it, and with this octane measure were uncovered interesting, valuable facts about gasoline. It was a bit dismaying to find that the normal paraffins, commonest of all hydrocarbons in most American petroleum, have a particular tendency to knock and so are comparatively poor motor fuel. The isoparaffins are better and the olefins still better. The naphthenes are excellent, but the aromatics best of all. Practical comparisons have been made between different types of hydrocarbons in rich and lean mixtures, at high and low speeds, under varying temperatures, and it has been established that the performance of gasoline depends largely upon the proportion of these different chemical groups which it contains.

When "gas" was a product of straight distillation, the hydrocarbons it contained and their proportions depended upon the crude oil fed to the still. The refiner had no control over the chemical character of his gasoline. Now this is all changed. Simple cracking produces a greater percentage of olefins than distillation. By controlling temperature and pressure and by use of different catalysts, it is now possible to break down the larger molecules and reform them so that the hydrocarbons in the finished gasoline may be quite different from the types in the raw material. Likewise, in building up petroleum gases into light liquids suitable for motor fuels, the reactions of polymerization and alkylation may be deliberately controlled to yield maximum quantities of the more desirable hydrocarbon groups.

Gasoline itself is subjected to re-forming operations and

by means of temperature, pressure, and catalysts the hydrocarbons present are modified. In this way paraffins are converted to the more desirable isoparaffins or even to the most desirable aromatics.

This chemicalization of oil refining has had two results. First, the octane rating of "regular gas" has moved up from 60 in 1932 to 75 at the time we entered this war. For the duration it has been forced back because of military needs. Even the chap who never could see the economy in premium gasoline has noticed the difference. The second effect has been a great increase in the output of high-octane gas — 90 or better — and a phenomenal reduction in its price. In 1937 we had a little 100-octane gas for test flights and engineering experiments. It cost $1 a gallon. In 1942, five years later, we were producing more than 20,000 gallons a day and the cost, wholesale, before taxes, was 20¢. How much more than that we are now producing is a deep secret, but it is a lot more. Not counting bombers and fighters, the Army alone is operating more than 1,200 cargo planes in transoceanic service, and on each long flight these giant airships must carry a greater weight of fuel than of cargo.

The 100-octane gas of today is a skillful blend of selected ingredients. The base is picked stock produced by the distillation of favored crudes, by catalytic cracking, by the isomerization of pentane and hexane, or by a mixture of these fuels. This stock is stepped up by adding synthetic blenders, iso-octane or isopentane, and tetraethyl lead.

So great is the need for the very essential ingredient iso-octane that it has been necessary to rob ordinary motor fuel and bottled gas for its raw materials. Tetraethyl lead is in the same critical position, which accounts for the disappearance of "ethyl gas" from your neighborhood service station.

Nevertheless, 100-octane gasoline is worth all it costs in additional plant, in extra labor, more time, and added expense. In the fighter plane it means speed, in the Flying Fortress, bombs; but, as the following table shows, it means more than these.

Aircraft	*87 Octane*	*100 Octane*
Max. speed at 2,750 rpm.	236 mph.	260 mph.
Altitude for max. speed	15,700 ft.	17,300 ft.
Cruising at 60% max. power	192 mph.	211 mph.
at height of	15,700 ft.	17,300 ft.
Rate of climb at sea level	1,490 ft./min.	2,180 ft./min.
Rate of climb at 19,500 ft.	1,220 ft./min.	2,050 ft./min.
Time of climb to 6,500 ft.	4.2 min.	2.9 min.
Time of climb to 26,000 ft.	19.4 min.	12.2 min.
Service ceiling	31,800 ft.	35,700 ft.
Absolute ceiling	32,800 ft.	36,700 ft.
Engine output	830 hp.	1,050 hp.

Add to the ravenous appetite of all our planes, tanks, jeeps, and transport vehicles for gasoline and lubricating-oils the need of the Navy for fuel oil, the demands for petroleum raw materials for TNT and for butadiene for the synthetic rubber, and you pile up a yearly total of more than 1,500,000,000 barrels — of 42 gallons each — as much petroleum as all the world produced in 1935.

To achieve this record we must press our oilwells to the limit as long as the war lasts. This brings twin Banquos shaking their grisly locks at the council tables of our petroleum industry.

Gone, long since, are the lush, wasteful days of that industry when gushers sprayed the countryside for miles around with an oily film and the gas burned brightly in torches. The unbridled flow of gas and oil has been harnessed and all sorts of clever mechanical devices catch and save these precious raw materials. Indeed, by scrupulously controlling the flow the quantity of both oil and gas to be recovered from a well has been materially increased, and varying with the conditions in the different fields the maximum total yield can be assured. Our petroleum industry is very conscious that in pushing production to meet war needs it is but robbing Peter to pay Paul, since maximum recovery is not achieved by these practices.

This sacrifice is inevitable, and nobody grumbles, but it points an admonitory finger straight at a historic milestone we are passing in the life of our petroleum production. It is a sign as little welcome as the first white hair on milady's pretty head, as disturbing as the first crack in the levee while the river rises behind.

Though we have shut our eyes to the unpleasant prospect of a dwindling petroleum supply, the facts we face are not a surprise. Back in 1936 Dr. Benjamin T. Brooks, a distinguished petroleum consultant of New York, and L. C. Snider, of the University of Texas, joined in a warning that "there is a possibility of a shortage of domestic petroleum as early as 1940, and a probability of a considerable shortage by 1945." Like Cassandra they were ridiculed by those who did not ignore their warning, but at the meeting of the American Petroleum Institute in Chicago, November 1942, a number of very responsible authorities stood up and sorrowfully sealed their prophecy.

The plain facts are that today we are producing about 4,000,000 barrels of crude a day, not enough oil, even with rationing, to supply the needs of the Army, Navy, lease-lend, and essential civilian driving. And the requirements of the armed forces are being written up and up, month after month, as the necessities of all-out bombing and air transport increase.

More than this, and in the long run more serious, for the past three years we have found less new oil than we have been consuming. The logical conclusion is as simple and as final as that five minus three equals two minus three equals minus one. The only unknown factor in that progressive subtraction is the duration of the war.

A number of things bound to happen to our petroleum situation after the war are fairly easy to foresee. Increased aviation will raise our gasoline consumption. Offsetting this to an unpredictable degree will be more efficient use of fuel in our internal-combustion engines. This will be a double-headed progress, in higher-octane gas, making possible greater compression, which means less gallons per ton-mile. There are definite limits to how far this boot-strap lifting will carry us.

It appears unlikely that we shall give over using liquid power; that is, unless some of the Sunday supplement dreams of grabbing the power of the sun or catching atomic power come true more promptly than seems scientifically possible. Undoubtedly we will have recourse to imported petroleum, first from South and Central America, later from the Middle East, eventually from Russia. From the Persian Gulf to the Arctic Circle is a vast territory of rich petroleum-bearing strata, a gigantic pool of yet uncharted reserves. It contains billions of barrels now hundreds of miles from any transportation.

When we remember our experience with nitrates in the last war and with rubber in this, it is disquieting to contemplate the day when we shall be dependent upon foreign sources for our petroleum, the single most vital raw material, as Graham Edgar put it, for the successful prosecution of modern war. One can indulge one's own fancy in picturing a world in which Russia is the sole great power with adequate domestic petroleum supplies.

Long before that time we shall have tapped our very considerable store of shale oil — the process is already available, but it cannot yet compete with gasoline — and we know how to make liquid fuel by the hydrogenation of coal, as Germany and England are doing today. The great vision of that aggressive chemurgist, Dr. William J. Hale, of liquid fuel from annually replaceable crops, alcohol by fermentation of grains and sugars, is still a third ace in the hole. Plainly the liquid-power sector of the chemical front is another scientific war that will not end at the peace table.

CHAPTER XVI

THE VIRTUE OF LEVITY

◇◇◇

"WE have always instinctively associated worth with weight, but we shall someday get an entirely new idea of values. Someday we shall free ourselves from the force of gravity by appreciating the merits of levity."

That day has come with dramatic suddenness. Its portentous meaning is being driven home by this technical war which in so many ways places a high premium upon the quality of lightness. In recent years there have been signs — sheer raincoats, feather-weight vacuum cleaners, the cargo plane, streamlined trains — which recall that daring prophecy made to me one glorious May day a quarter of a century ago.

It was the first spring after the first World War. Like all American industry, the Dow Chemical Company was in the throes of transition to peacetime production. Some plant units were busy. Others were shut down. Some were being revamped, while a few were being scrapped. We had spent the morning on an inspection tour, and Herbert H. Dow, the company's founder and then active head, had explained the specific whys and wherefores of all these busy changes. After lunch we went out into his beloved garden, and, sitting in comfortable rustic chairs on a little

224]

hillock overlooking row after row of his apple trees all in bloom, he talked of many things.

"From diamonds to iron ore," continued Dr. Dow, "we have always weighed our values. Only cork for life-preservers and feathers for down comforters have been in demand because they were positively light. More than that, since long ages before the Great Pyramid and the ponderous Roman aqueducts, size and solidity have indicated strength and durability.

"But to move two pounds takes twice as much energy as to move one. Slowly we are learning that by the right choice of materials and better design lightness can be achieved without sacrifice of strength or durability. Why waste money and energy struggling against gravity? After all, levity may be a positive virtue. It is certainly a great convenience.

"Once we get that idea into our heads we are bound to rush forward on a new line of progress. The changes it will bring will be quite as great as those that followed the first use of metals; must more revolutionary than communism. I don't dare dream what this fundamentally different conception will mean to mechanics and chemistry; what it will do to transportation, to our ways of living, to our whole economic system, what its effects will be upon our political, legal, and social structures."

It is here, that revolution. Though we still grope blindly to fathom its meaning, any of us can now recognize it. As Dr. Dow foresaw so clearly, the airplane has dramatized the value of lightness, and in doing so it has ushered in the new era of plastics and light-weight metals.

It was Dr. Dow's philosophy of levity, translated into

action, that started the Dow Chemical Company on the production of magnesium, the lightest of all structural metals, and, despite many setbacks, has kept it in the business during a score of years when profits never balanced the accumulated costs of research and development.

During World War I there was a sudden demand for magnesium, not as a light-weight metal, but for flares. The old magnesium ribbon of the photographer's flashlight had enlisted in the Army. The price was then about $5 a pound, and Dow, General Electric, and several others went in for its production. Only Dow persisted after the war.

As early as 1912 Dr. Dow, in his systematic exploration of the chemical components of the Michigan brines that lay beneath the plant, began separating out the magnesium and calcium chlorides. Several thousand tons of magnesium chloride were then being imported as an ingredient in architectural stuccoes, and when the supply was cut off by hostilities Dow began filling this demand.

On the desk of Willard Dow, son of Herbert Dow and his successor, sits a little, dull-gray cone of metal, a sample of the first batch of magnesium made at Midland during July 1916. It had been produced in a 100-pound steel pot by Professor Veazey of Case, working with others under the direction of Edwin O. Barstow in the Dow laboratories. That initial trial was not very encouraging. Six months later, however, at a cost of $225,000, an electrolytic magnesium plant had been built. It operated 30 hours. Then the cells froze and choking chlorine fumes drove everyone pellmell out of the new building. Within another six months that balky process had been tamed, and the regular production of magnesium metal begun.

There was then, 1920, practically no commercial use of magnesium metal and no knowledge of how it could be employed. Accordingly, in the Dow laboratories an exhaustive study was begun of its properties and hundreds of magnesium alloys were prepared and their properties also measured and tested. On another visit to Midland, I remember a score of automobile engines lined up on blocks around a big bare room, all running merrily, testing magnesium pistons for performance against the ordinary pistons of cast iron. To lighten the weight of reciprocal working parts was an obvious advantage, and since war days John Hoy, working on the foundry techniques of handling this strange metal, had been co-operating with Ford in the development of the Liberty motor. Practical experience in casting magnesium was sorely needed, and this Vermont Yankee, who delighted to pose as a tough guy, but for whose funeral, when he died, all the churches of Midland eagerly fought, learned the first lessons of magnesium fabrication the hard way in a crude little experimental foundry. In the meantime, the methods of extracting the magnesium chloride from the brine and isolating the metal from this salt by electrolysis were being constantly improved.

Out of all this hard work came important discoveries. At the end of ten years the Dow Chemical Company had admittedly the best magnesium extraction process. Until today, May 1943, it is the sole process that has continuously produced the light metal on a commercial basis in the United States. The company's metallurgists had found a whole series of magnesium alloys, patented under the name of Dowmetal, and, thanks to the researches headed

by that high-strung self-starter John A. Gann and later
by the inspiring Don Hanawalt, had stored up the biggest
fact-pile about the metal's corrosion and fatigue and its
behavior in thousands of checked alloys. The tricky fabrication of magnesium had been accomplished.

By the early '30's magnesium was ready to go, but push
and shove as the Dow organization might, the dead weight
of metallurgical inertia could not be budged. The price
had been brought down to 30¢ a pound, less than a tenth
of the old war level, and on a volume basis it was conpeti-
tive with aluminum. Dow dug up scores of logical uses.
The metal-working trades and the metal-using industries
shrugged their shoulders and said: "So what?" The Army
and Navy, which now so clamorously cry for more and
more magnesium, simply could not be interested. Nobody
yet appreciated the virtue of levity.

During these discouraging years Dow's sole American
competitor, the American Magnesium Company, a subsidiary of the Aluminum Company of America, which had
been smelting magnesium from magnesite, gave up production and began buying from Dow what it needed as
an alloying ingredient. Naturally, in so dead a market a
five-year sales contract was negotiated at a preferential
price. The companies also sensibly agreed to avoid threatened suits by exchanging certain fabrication patents which
were questionably in interference with each other but
which might have held up the development of the use of
magnesium.

Still the stockpile of the light metal was growing at Midland. Accordingly, between 1934 and 1938, Dow was very
glad to sell some 6,000,000 pounds to Germany at a bar-

gain price of 22½¢ as against 27¢ to smaller contract customers. At this time the total sales of magnesium in this
country were less than 1,500,000 pounds a year and our
Army and Navy were interested only in insignificant quantities for flares.

Although Dow had repeatedly, stoutly refused to enter
into any patent pools with the German I.G., which had
such agreements with the Aluminum Company and its
magnesium subsidiary, Thurman Arnold, when he brought
suit on behalf of the Government to abrogate these international agreements, deduced from these prices a conspir-
acy to hold up magnesium prices in this country and restrict its domestic production. Such preferential prices to
big buyers are common in all fields, especially when supply
exceeds demand, and at that time any agreement to restrict
magnesium output in this country had about as much logic
as for you and me to agree not to eat more than a dozen
eggs for breakfast during the next six months. A great
point was made of the fact that before the war emergency
Dow never produced more than 4,400,000 pounds of the
metal in any year. But in none of those years did domestic
sales reach half of this total. Till the Nazi war machine
rolled out under an airplane cover and behind incendiary-
bomb softening, nobody here had any appreciation of the
virtue of levity.

As late as 1938 the total civilian use of magnesium was
still less than 3,000,000 pounds a year. The Army and Navy
had found no other use than in flares. When the war clouds
threatened, the next year, Dow had a stockpile of 5,000,000
pounds, nearly two years' supply, and a capacity to make
6,000,000. Yet upon its own initiative it increased that ca-

pacity to 12,000,000 pounds, or five full years' supply.

Ten years before, to meet the demand for bromine in the preparation of ethyl gas, this company, which started as an extractor of bromine from the Michigan brines, put into operation on the North Carolina coast a plant to extract this element from seawater. It had evolved a similar process for the recovery of magnesium from the ocean. In January 1940, four months before President Roosevelt appeared before Congress with a plea for his defense program, Dow broke ground at the mouth of the Brazos River, near Freeport, Texas, for a seawater magnesium plant. This had a projected capacity of 24,000,000 pounds, trebling the country's output. A similar expansion of its foundry capacity was undertaken; a new rolling-mill started; and the magnesium output at the home plant was boosted by 50 per cent. In November 1941 — just before the unexpected shock of December 7 — plans were approved to raise the Freeport plant's capacity to 36,000,000 pounds. Up to this time $25,000,000 of company money had been spent on this expanded defense work magnesium program. Because of this expansion, by June 1941 Dow was producing at the rate of 30,000,000 pounds a year, fifteen times as much as two years before.

Since the Office of Production Management and the War Production Board have taken charge of the war effort, Dow has three times stepped up its production capacity at Freeport. It has also furnished the know-how to other companies working its process in the war effort. Now, a year and a half after the declaration of war, this single company has supplied 90 per cent of our magnesium. Alone that would be an "E" flag accomplishment, but, like all chemi-

SAMPLING BRASS FOR ANALYSIS.

cal companies, Dow makes many products, and most of them — some four pounds out of every five — go directly to the chemical front. That is probably a fair average for the entire chemical industry, and the diversity of its war-chemicals output, the multiplicity of their uses, and the initiative displayed in the tremendous expansion are also typical of its peers and competitors. As the chemist himself says, "Let's see a representative sample."

A year before Pearl Harbor, when the rubber and petroleum companies were getting nowhere fast trying to interest somebody in Washington in a synthetic rubber program, Dow already had a year's plant experience on butadiene tucked away and a whole year earlier had produced and sold styrene, the co-ingredient of butadiene in the famous Buna S. During that year it made two additions to its butadiene operations, installed plants for ethylene glycol (anti-freeze in airplane engines), for ethylene (plastics and Thiokol rubber substitutes), for graphite (lubricants), for additional Thiokol, more power, more chlorine, and a new metallurgical laboratory.

During the first year of the war it expanded its capacity for phenol (picric acid and plastics), aniline oil (coal-tar intermediate), iodine, chloroform, styrene, magnesium alloys, and chlorine, and undertook the manufacture of hexachlorethane (smoke screens) and monochloracetic acid (vitamins). Besides this, it has built a defense plant to produce chlorobenzene and a Chemical Warfare Service plant for direct war chemicals.

Not until the British had shot down a couple of Messerschmitts were the merits of magnesium fully recognized. The 180 pounds of magnesium used in a representative airplane engine saves 90 pounds as against aluminum and 500 pounds as against steel. Even against its closest light-weight rival the saving in a four-motor bomber means two more men, or 42 gallons of gas, or 360 pounds in bombs.

That drives home the importance of levity, but magnesium has other uses. It is needed, as we have seen, for incendiary bombs. Almost as much of the metal as we used previous to the war is now needed for military fireworks, signal flares, star shells, flash bombs. Besides, there are the tracer-shells for anti-aircraft defense and the tracer-bullets in every fifth cartridge of the machine-gun belts. No wonder the War Production Board made strenuous efforts to boost the output of the lightest of metals.

Two alkali-makers, Mathieson and Diamond, are taking waste calcium chloride from their processes and with the magnesium in dolomite producing magnesium chloride, which is treated by the Dow process. The same operation is projected at Austin, Texas, working up waste magnesium chloride from the potash mines of the Union Potash Company at Carlsbad, New Mexico. At Las Vegas, in Nevada, the Basic Magnesium Company is working to duplicate a British process starting with the mineral magnesite, and out at Permanente, California, the dynamic Henry Kaiser has his own troubles with an Austrian process devised by Fritz Hansgirg. This has been operated with indifferent success in England and Japan, but it has a habit of blowing up at inopportune moments.

Of the various new processes, however, the one wise metallurgists find most promising came out of Canada, the discovery of a minister's son who partly paid his way through McGill University playing in a jazz band, the pleasant, good-looking, versatile Dr. Lloyd M. Pidgeon. Later he won an Oxford scholarship and on his return to Canada joined the Canadian National Research Council. His magnesium idea was simple and seemed sensible. He proposed to smelt burnt dolomite, the commonest and most widely distributed magnesium-bearing mineral, with ferrosilicon. This would release the magnesium from combination with oxygen in the form of vapor which could be condensed and recovered as solid crystalline metal of very high purity, essentially the process of zinc smelting.

General McNaughton, then head of the Canadian Research Council, now Commander in Chief of the Canadian Forces, was interested. He left his technical post to take up military duties, however, and the Pidgeon process sorely lacked influential friends. Two United States Bureau of Mines men had figured it out on paper and in an official bulletin declared that it just would not work, and no company could be interested. But Pidgeon had plenty of tenacity. He found as backers two natural-born gamblers.

They seem an ill-assorted pair. Bob Jowsey is a typical, old-time prospector, a big two-fisted Scot, the kind you call a "character." He knows every mining man in Canada by his first name, and everyone in the country knows him and links his name with Coronation Gulf and God's Lake. It is significant that he was the first man to use caterpillar tractors over frozen lakes and rivers for hauling mine supplies into the bush. Walter Segsworth is a detailist, a precise man, always a rugged independent, who made his first strike in silver in the Cobalt country and who is president of the Moneta Porcupine mines.

Gold mining was out for the duration and both turned to other minerals. Both wanted to help the war effort. They knew the crying need for the light metal and they learned about Dr. Pidgeon. Segsworth, the trained engineer, scrupulously examined the inventor's voluminous records. To his "gold is where you find it" mind the records pointed to a sound possibility.

On a hunch that this process was a good gamble, they went to a common friend, Thayer Lindsley, president of Ventures, Ltd., a mineral prospecting company, a third good gambler, but an exceedingly sound financial man. He had developed the profitable Falconbridge nickel property, where there was supposed to be but little nickel. The three wrote checks to pay for a sizable experimental plant, and called in American consultants, Singmaster and Breyer, to check the trials. Breyer, a hardheaded enthusiast, and his conservative partner Singmaster had been reared in the zinc industry, and their opinion would thus be doubly valuable. With the Breyer O.K., the triumvirate, incorporated as Dominion Magnesium, Ltd., went ahead to construct a Canadian plant, now in complete operation, after the three biggest financial and electrical smelting interests in Canada had turned it down. Five Pidgeon plants are in operation in the United States: Ford at Dearborn, Michigan; National Lead at Luckey, Ohio; New England Lime at Canaan, Connecticut; American Metals at Wingdale, New York; and Henry Kaiser at Manteca, near Stockton, California. The combined output is to be 90,000,000 pounds.

With a postwar output which may reach a hundred times the prewar total, we shall have an abundance of this feather-weight champion among the metals to indulge our new appreciation of lightness. It sells now for 20½¢ a pound. It will sell more cheaply then, well down into the price range of household utility. The war is teaching many new ways in which magnesium can be employed. In the Wright aeronautical engine, for example, there are 159 magnesium parts: super-charger covers, intake manifolds, pistons, oil pumps, ventilators, and a host of little parts down to wing nuts.

We are just beginning to grasp the reality of Dr. Dow's prophecy of revolutionary change. A destroyer built of magnesium in place of steel might be expected to make a speed of 50 miles an hour skimming over the surface of the water. No longer will it be necessary to haul two tons of freight car to transport a single ton of goods. A grand piano that a husky man could lift himself is possible. If you have caught the great vision of levity, you can dream your own dreams. If you want something definite to sink your teeth into, remember that a foot-square cube of brass weighs 525 pounds; of steel, 487 pounds; of aluminum, 169 pounds; and of magnesium, only 112 pounds.

CHAPTER XVII

CATS IN THE BAG

◇◇

AT Massacre Bay, Attu Island, stores for the invasion troops were being unloaded: food, ammunition, medical supplies, and four long packing-cases that looked like gigantic florists' boxes. These cases contained, not a gross of long-stemmed American Beauty roses, but each a 1943-model American machine gun. It was a cold, nasty job. The small boat pitched like a bronco. The rocky beach was slippery with ice and slush. Wet, benumbed fingers clutched desperately, but one of those long, unwieldy boxes slipped overboard.

Six months earlier that would have been a serious accident, in the foggy, freezing atmosphere of the Aleutians, a minor tragedy, for seawater does not improve intricate, swift-moving metal mechanisms and a machine gun that jams at critical moments is curses and possibly casualties. But these machine guns were vacuum-packed in cellophane, literally so, and such tragedies have been eliminated.

Only a few seasons ago Bayard Okie, that original genius of window display, jolted the jaded interest of New York Christmas shoppers by wrapping an automobile in trans-

parent film tied up with Gargantuan bows of red ribbons.
It was a clever stunt with a suggestive Christmas-present
appeal and it registered a new high for a wrapping-mate-
rial already used for almost everything from prunes to
pianos.

It was only a few years before Okie's sensational pack-
aged motor car that a chemistry professor at Antioch College applied a familiar bit of chemical knowledge to start
a sideline venture that has grown into a neat little business.
His friends say William Archie Hammond was tempted
into this commercial field in order to satisfy his passion for
early editions of McGuffey readers in mint condition, a
hobby that does not accord comfortably with the salary
of an assistant professor. After graduation from Miami and
a Ph.D. from Ohio State, this chemical Kentuckian served
in the first World War in the Chemical Warfare Service,
then with a cement company, and finally for five years as
chief chemist of the United States Gypsum Company. Before going to Antioch he did another five years of consulting work, specializing in the processes and byproducts of
the ceramics industry. Out of this experience grew the idea
of applying the well-known ability of anhydrous calcium
sulphate — bone-dry gypsum — to absorb moisture for a lot
of miscellaneous uses as a drying-agent.

With his professional background Hammond went about
this job of commercial exploitation in a somewhat unusual
way. He did coin a trade-name, but he made no secret of
what his material was, relying upon an exceptionally pure
grade, offering it in granule, powder, and cake forms, and
playing up the possibility of using chrome salts as indica-
tors that turn from blue to red on the absorption of mois-

ture. He began in 1935, selling chiefly to laboratories where microscopes and certain chemically pure reagents must be stored in a desert-dry atmosphere. Bit by bit he extended his market even into the packaging-field.

A synthesis of these ideas — vacuum packing in a transparent film, protected from moisture by calcium sulphate that telltales by a red color when all is not well — has been applied to war uses that promise to do a good many things to packaging in the postwar days. These developments have initiated several activities on the chemical front. The production of this desiccant grade of calcium sulphate has jumped a thousandfold within the year. It is being pressed into cakes of many shapes and sizes to fit, for example, into the place of spark-plugs in both airplane and motor-car engines, to slide into the firing-chambers of guns, to pack snugly around all sorts of metal parts. For the wrapping new types of transparent film have been perfected, notably Pliofilm, a latex-base material, and ethyl cellulose, both of which are now being produced in sheets of unheard-of dimensions. Airplane engines can be wrapped in them.

These new methods of packing engines and tools and replacement parts prevent the attack of moisture by excluding it. They are effective even under as different, exacting conditions as the foggy Aleutians and the steaming Solomons. Formerly all engines, tools, and spare parts were coated heavily with grease to prevent rusting. Thorough cleaning with some grease-cutting solvent was necessary before they could be assembled or used. Properly to clean a tommy gun, for example, took a bucket of carbon tetrachloride and half a day's industrious work of two men. Now it can be taken from its modern wrappings, assembled, and put into action in a few minutes: a better job, done better, and more quickly by applying these chemical ideas.

We have become familiar with makeshift packages, many of them designed to substitute for scarce, imported tin, others to save glass, or to conserve space and weight, thus offsetting the limitations of restricted wartime shipping. A number of these innovations will persist. For years talkative speculation has been popular about what this tin-can-addicted people will do when this steadily diminishing metal really becomes scarce and high-priced. Ideas about plastics and lacquered cardboard have been tried out, but it took the war to give these experiments a nation-wide test. Some of the returns already in make a little forecasting not too hazardous, and various treated paper-boards, transparent wrappings for dried foods, the square rather than the round container, are all perfectly safe bets for the future.

Necessity's children flourish under war conditions. We are compelled, willy-nilly, to make changes and adopt substitutes that stimulate invention and force trials nobody would dare attempt in normal times. All the bold innovators of thought, word, and deed have learned, often to their despair, that for all his reputation as a curious and adaptable biped man is a most conservative animal with a distressing disinclination to try anything new for the first time. His food habits are particularly fixed. If, as Swift surmised, it was a bold man who first ate an oyster, it takes a desperate one to switch from wheat to corn or vice versa. War eggs us on to such desperate deeds. The last war introduced American corn, which Europeans perversely per-

sist in calling more correctly "maize," into large areas of
the older continent as food for both man and beast, and
one of the effects of this war, from which our grandchil-
dren will profit greatly and whose beginning they will
never remember, will be dehydrated and debulked food.

In his desperate need, one of the first means to save
from crop to crop that man learned was drying. The jerked
venison of our own forefathers represented a trick of dehydration over an open fire that they learned from the In-
dians, and the humble prune has a story that begins well
back in the B.C. epoch. But modern dehydration is something quite different, "drying with a college education,"
an education gained in the laboratories.

It began during the last war, when it inspired the 467th
verse of the doughboy's classic:

> They feed us carrots every day
> That taste just like alfalfa hay.
> Hinkey, dinkey, parlez-vous.

Unfortunately there was more truth than poetry in that
song, but saving the savor of fresh food is not the only improvement that has been made. The 8,905,158 pounds of
dehydrated food produced for the Army during World
War I was sadly lacking in vitamins and other nutritive
elements, lost or destroyed in the crude processing. This
year, 1943, we shall produce more than 450,000,000 pounds
of dehydrated foods of top quality as to flavor and food
value. That will require three-fourths of all the vegetables
we usually pack in tin cans, one egg in every three, 60 per
cent of our total cheese output, 80 per cent of our tinned
salmon; but it will release 200,000,000 pounds of metal,

save nine out of ten cargo ships, feed our troops and our allies better than they could possibly be served were we trying to ship fresh foods.

As in food, so also in rubber the war is forcing a revolution that goes on under our eyes without catching our attention. The great synthetic rubber program and our tire troubles have stolen the spotlight, but literally thousands of tons of the natural elastic gum are being saved by substitutions in less publicized applications. The vague borderlines between resins, plastics, waxes, and elastomers are revealing new promises. Ethyl cellulose, a well-known plastic, for example, may be transformed into a rubbery material by treatment with castor oil. This "ethyl rubber" serves well for fruit-jar seals, baby pants, cushions, and scores of other little, but necessary uses. Electrical battery boxes, traditionally made of hard rubber, are now made of celluloid with such success that this is likely to be a lasting replacement. The plastic is quite as resistant to acid and it has the advantage of being transparent and tougher to the drop test. The highly polished surfaces of the large transparent sections of planes must be protected from scratching during shipment and assembly. Strips of paper were formerly applied over them and held in place by rubber cement, which adheres to the plastic surface closely yet peels off quickly and cleanly. Du Pont researchers made more than 100 different adhesives before they found one that met these specifications. Again the replacement outdoes the old material in that the paper strips may be re-used if necessary, and the new adhesive does not crack off under extreme cold nor does it age so rapidly.

Rubber treated with chlorine becomes a sirupy material

that in recent years has enjoyed fast-growing employment in paints for concrete and stucco, in lacquers, printing-inks, coated papers, textiles. Its flexibility and water- and filmproofing qualities are very widely valuable. Late in 1941 the Hercules Powder Company, which makes this product under the trade-name Parlon, was urged by the War Production Board to expand this production to meet the increased needs of the Quartermaster General. Parlon was the backbone of the Government program for flameproofing Army duck.

A big new plant was being built, with a capacity of some 4,000,000 pounds of chlorinated rubber a year. Then the rubber crisis — it takes a pound of high-grade crepe rubber to produce about three pounds of this chlorinated rubber — forced the Quartermaster General to abandon Parlon for flameproofing textiles. The company was caught flatfooted with a $1,000,000 investment on its shoulders. But there was a shortage of chlorinated paraffin wax. Accordingly, Assistant Manager Clark Kingery of the Parlon plant began a day-and-night bout on April 20, 1942, to convert to a new raw material and a new process.

By May 8 the plant staff felt confident enough to start a 7,500-pound batch in the chlorinators. During the month of May the output of the new product was 212,000 pounds; two months later it had grown to 1,206,000 pounds. The shortage of chlorinated paraffin had been broken and a suitable substitute had arrived for waterproofing and flameproofing Army tents and the tarpaulins for protecting big guns, stores of supplies, motor cars, airplanes, and whatnot.

This whole matter of chemically treated fabrics has been shoved ahead many years by Mars' imperious demands. Although much improved in the past years, treatments for preshrinking, to prevent wrinkles and creases, to moth-proof fabrics have not always lived up to all our hopes, but great progress is being made for the benefit of the sol-diers and sailors. Civilians must now await their turn, but it will come soon after the end of hostilities, for the new chemical processes are getting a splendid tryout on a big scale and under all sorts of conditions.

About the time the war broke out, one of these new de-velopments was being promoted by a big, red-headed boomer, a successful chemical specialty man. The experi-ence of Harry Wiberg reveals how easy it is to guess the wrong market for a new chemical product.

Using as a base an emulsion of aluminum acetate, he perfected a temporary water-repellent compound which coats cloth with a protective film that withstands such nasty stains as iodine and tomato ketchup. It washes out in the next laundering, but it carries with it the stains and grime that it held on the surface. So the enthusiastic Wi-berg went out to sell the laundries of his native Los Angeles. They were completely uninterested. All his best sales arguments seemed merely to increase their deadly apathy. At the end of his third interview he was sure that he was on the wrong track. So he went to the big hotels and hospitals, which were very much interested. The fact that his Stainpruf lengthened the life of a hotel tablecloth by 25 per cent meant something to these institutional laundries, and he has them so well sold that now the regular commercial laundries are beginning to offer this treatment of table linens, sport clothes, and furniture slipcovers as a special extra service.

Another type of protective finish has been perfected during the war by du Pont for a strictly war use. Cotton camouflage nets are treated by padding and drying in moderate heat with a fire-, water-, and weather-resistant finish that comes in sand and olive-drab shades. The Army Engineers have tested this camouflage finish and found that it remains flexible in subzero weather and yet is not sticky when the thermometer touches 100 in the shade. Treatment of shade cloth for the tobacco fields is indicated as one peacetime use.

Synthetic fibers are not escaping the quickening touch. Before the war tires with rayon fabric had so thoroughly demonstrated their superior wearing qualities that they had been first choice for heavy duty on busses and tractors. For this purpose Cordura, a special rayon woven of a tightly twisted, heavy filament which was developed by du Pont, is specified, but even its remarkable performance is said to be bettered by tire fabric made of nylon.

Just before our declaration of war one of the tire companies fabricated four dozen big-bomber tires upon a nylon base and shipped them for testing to Wright Field. They were installed on planes that soon took off for the battlefront. And what a year of torturous testing these tires had!

A bomber tire on active service must take wicked punishment. The big plane, weighing 25 tons or more, comes swooping down to a small improvised landing-field. From a speed up to 100 miles an hour, it must, to borrow a saying from the stables, stop and turn on the head of a water bucket. The nylon tires can take it.

In the testing-laboratory, too, they have taken the so-called bruise test in which a blunt, cone-shaped plunger is pushed down upon the tread of an inflated tire until it bursts. Applied to a 9-inch tire made of the strongest materials in commercial use, the test plunger sank 6 inches before the tire burst. Applied to a 9-inch nylon tire, inflated to identical pressure, the plunger forced the tread clear to the rim without bursting, and when the plunger was withdrawn the tire sprang back to its original shape without showing a sign of injury. So it appears that the improved synthetic rubbers, which the chemists promise us, are not to be the sole means of getting the postwar motorist greater mileage and better tire service.

Nylon has another fresh application due to another of those curious, little-known shortages for which we can thank the Japs. During the long, cold winters, the wide-ranging hogs of Siberia and northern Mongolia grow the best bristles in the world, the longest, thickest, toughest — raw material for all our high-grade paintbrushes. Nylon had already proved its worth in the toothbrush, but a paint-brush must have a long, resilient bristle with a tapering end to promote the smooth, easy flow of the paint to the receiving surface. Nylon was tough and springy, but that finely tapering end was essential.

While the synthetic fiber could easily be cut any desired length, still extruded nylon was as straight and blunt as so many sticks of macaroni. To a master painter, who cherishes his pet brushes for their whip and snap, a straight, stiff bristle was a sacrilege. And yet an extruded fiber does not of necessity have to be of uniform thickness. One modification of the rayon filament that gives it versatility to create novel effects depends upon regular variations in thickness. This is accomplished by the purely physical operation of changing the tension upon the filaments as they are drawn through the spinnerets by altering the speed of the revolving spool upon which they are collected out of the final processing-bath. If alternate thickness and thinness might be rigidly controlled as to both diameter and exact spacing, and then if the filaments might be accurately, automatically cut exactly at the points to maximum thickness and thinness, an artificial taper might be given these cut staples of nylon. Two little "ifs," and the Siberian hog would have a real rival housed right in American factories.

Two du Point scientists have removed those "ifs," the big, blond Willard Crane, a chemical engineer trained at the University of Cincinnati, and thin, wiry Ruben Fields, a mathematician who graduated from Syracuse. To get a uniformly alternating thick-and-thin thread they tried out all sorts of eccentric, even cloverleaf, cams. Finally they solved the problem mathematically on paper and in the machine with a complicated planetary gear that scrupulously regulates the tension on the filament. Revolving razor blades synchronized with the speed of the filaments cut them at the points of greatest thickness and thinness. As an extra precaution this cutting is guarded by an electric eye to compensate even the tiniest fraction of variation of the prospective bristles.

It was not a simple task, for nylon fibers are themselves stretched to give them their famous elasticity. Accordingly,

this controlled variable speed of pulling — low speed for
the thick portion, high speed for the thin — had to be
hooked up behind the stretching operation and must be
accomplished without snapping the almost microscopic
filaments at their thin points. The tapered nylon bristle
crowned five years of intensive research. Fortunately it
culminated just at the time we lost contact with the Ori-
ental source of supply, and for the duration the output of
two new du Pont plants is pre-empted by the Government,
chiefly for the Navy and the shipbuilding yards.

Some 5,000,000 pounds of bristle are required by our
brush manufacturers every year and more than half goes
into paintbrushes. The natural bristles sell for $12 to $18
a pound. Already the nylon bristles are priced a third less.
Yet on actual working test they deliver more than three
times the wear, which is a ninefold net increase in value.
Furthermore, nylon comes to the brush-maker ready and
properly sized to be put into the handles, while the natural bristles must be cleaned, disinfected, trimmed and
sized, graded according to diameter, degrees of stiffness,
and color, then sorted and collected in a "formula" for a
given style and price of brush. These many tedious processes are performed mostly by hand and consume much
time and labor.

Nylon in another form — the straight, solid mono-fila-
ments that formerly went into fishing-leaders and tennis-
racket strings — is replacing another natural raw material
formerly a monopoly of the Japanese. Stockings are more
glamorous than surgical sutures, but there is no comparison as to their relative importance these days. Although
nylon stockings are "out," it is comforting to know that

millions of feet of nylon sutures are ready to take the place of the silk threads formerly used.

The surgeons are also reporting another superior replacement, for they like to use as small a suture as possible, and since nylon exceeds silk in tensile strength and can be produced in definite, uniform diameters, it gives them the finest possible threads. The solid strands of nylon are also less irritating to wounded tissue and, being inert to moisture and germs, they are valuable for "stay sutures" needed for heavy wounds and for use within the human body. To cap all, nylon, unlike silk, neither dries out nor rots even when stored indefinitely under the most adverse climatic conditions.

Chemists have been improving other tools of the surgeon, and it is not a little thing that the "stickum" of the good old adhesive bandage has also been rendered weatherproof. In the tropics, in the Arctic, even, as we have sadly learned, inside the family medicine chest right here within the United States, the adhesive properties of this useful tape do deteriorate: it becomes either too soft and sticky or dries out to lose any semblance of stick-to-itiveness. Adding a small percentage of Staybelite to the adhesive paste mixture preserves its original properties. Staybelite is a very fine, light grade of wood rosin, not affected by the oxygen of the air, that is specially prepared by the Hercules Powder Company.

More important are improvements in the first-aid dressings used on wounds and burns. A number of new sulfadrug dressings, from salves to soluble tapes of ethyl cellulose, are now available, and quite recently — too soon yet for much clinical testing — three pathologists of Wayne

University, Dave Brady, Robert Bauer, and Frederick
Yonkman, have perfected another of these soothing healing preparations. They dissolve sulfanilamide and sulfathiazole, the strong infection-fighters, in propylene glycol,
a chemical kinsman of glycerin, and then add a solution of
the plastic material alkyl cellulose. This mixture sprayed
on loose gauze makes a durable, antiseptic, healing bandage that is elastic, soft, and easily removed.

Too new, or rather in too scanty supply, for widespread
application at the present time, the most powerful of all
bacteria-destroyers has apparently been found in penicillin. On any number of counts it is a unique chemotherapeutic agent. So great is its potency that even in a dilution
of one part in 100,000,000 it destroys bacteria, yet it seems
to be quite harmless to man. It outdoes the sulfa-drugs and
is most effective against the deadly pus-formers, the staphylococci, among them the cause of that curse of the battlefields, gas gangrene. Most remarkable of all, it is an excre-
tion produced in the life processes of the common bread
mold, *Penicillium notatum,* after which it has been named.

In St. Mary's Hospital, London, back in 1929, Dr. Alex-
ander Flemming, professor of bacteriology at the University of London, noticed a small clear spot on the surface
of a nutrient liquid in which he was growing a culture of
billions of staphylococci. It roused his eager scientific curiosity, and he marveled to find in the center a tiny colony of
penicillium. It seemed that the mold, whose spores are
found in the air everywhere, inhibited in some way the
growth of the cocci around it.

Flemming deliberately repeated the chance experiment
by planting penicillium in coccus cultures and he ob-

served the same results. He went further and attempted to put this observation to practical use, publishing his findings in a solid 10-page article in the highly professional *British Journal of Experimental Pathology*, under the ultra-scientific title "On the Antibacterial Action of Cultures of a Penicillium with Special Reference to Their Use in the Isolation of B. influenza."

That workmanlike article did not stir up a sensation. Nobody suspected a new chemotherapeutic agent. In fact, at that time very few pathologists or chemists or physicians gave any thought to chemotherapy. The sulfa-drugs dramatically awoke this interest, and three years ago Dr. H. W. Florey in the Sir William Dunn School of Pathology reobserved this antibacterial action of molds. Digging through the literature for leads, he found not only Flemming's article, but an even earlier one by two French workers, Gratia and Darth, who had reported that *Penicillium glaucum* destroys the savage bacteria of anthrax.

Inspired by these hints, a team of Oxford researchers put in months of hard work at the end of which they had isolated and collected from hundreds of penicillium cultures a tiny pinch of yellow crystals which they found enormously destructive to many micro-organisms. They tried it out in test tubes, in mice, and finally in man. Their big problem was to get sufficient quantities of this powerful chemical, and they sent a hurry call for help to the National Research Council in Washington. Under its auspices Merck & Company and E. R. Squibb & Sons are collaborating in the most carefully conducted development of one of the most difficult chemical-manufacturing operations ever undertaken.

Ordinary chemical operations are not at all like the preparation of penicillin. The mold is grown in a sugary nutrient solution in bottles. These are stacked in racks, as in a great wine cellar, where the temperature and humidity are controlled at what checked experience has demonstrated to give optimum conditions for growth. Yellow droplets of penicillin develop on the mold and filter down into the nutrient solution. This is decanted off and the chemical is removed by an elaborate process of evaporation. After 12 days' incubation about 40 gallons of mold culture are collected, from which in the end only 10 grams of penicillin are recovered.

Day and night, efforts are being made to improve this yield, to simplify the technique, to find more productive strains of molds, to unravel the chemical puzzle of the formula and molecular structure of penicillin itself. Progress seems slow, but month after month new facts accumulate. In the meantime the output of this newest of germ-destroyers is steadily increasing. Practically all the current production is going to the armed forces.

Much must still be learned about penicillin. Two earnestly sought facts are its exact chemical composition and the precise means by which it destroys bacteria. Until the first is determined there is, of course, no possibility of manufacturing it synthetically as so many of the vitamins are now produced in great quantities. It is obviously a complex compound, and years may go by before it can be duplicated in the test tube. However, it is being subjected to searching studies by scores of competent chemists, bacteriologists, and pathologists armed with the latest scientific equipment. In the end, possibly sooner than anyone dares now to hope, its chemical riddle will be solved.

Strictly speaking, penicillin, like the sulfa-drugs, is not a germ-killer. In ways now obscure to us these chemotherapeutic agents inhibit the normal activities of these dangerous micro-organisms. Why and how? Do they starve them out by upsetting their digestive processes, or by poisoning their food, or by destroying their powers of assimilation? Do they prevent their multiplication by some sort of bacterial birth control? Do they perchance check their toxic effects by some deadly disturbance of their metabolism? If we but knew, we should be able more intelligently to attack the bacteria. If in addition we had learned the whys and wherefores of the unfavorable effects these drugs have upon their human hosts, we should have gone a long way towards removing these toxic effects.

These answers will be found by biochemists and pathologists, and the opportunities before penicillin are assuredly as great as those yet to be realized by the sulfa-drugs. Literally thousands of different sulfa-compounds are possible and more than 400 distinct species of molds have been classified. Hasty, preliminary study points straight to other medicinal chemicals from different members of this large, universal family.

These discoveries cut a wide path through the tangled jungle of diseases in which medicine has been groping towards the horizon Pasteur located when he discovered the true nature of the bacteria. Ehrlich's vision of chemicals to kill all disease germs is now a very tangible, attainable objective.

CHAPTER XVIII

THE MASTER-KEY

◇◇◇

In their red-plush, carved-oak sanctum the Senate Finance
Committee was holding hearings on the rewriting of a new
tariff to meet the changed conditions that followed the
first World War. The proceedings had been long drawn
out. The testimony bristled with technicalities not easy to
assimilate and interpret justly. The hearings had developed the inevitable clashes of conflicting interests. A presi-
dential election was in the offing and the political situation
was tense. The Committee members were tired yet eager
to get this tedious business of fact-finding finished.

In the straight-backed witness chair sat a young busi-
nessman who made a distinctly favorable impression. He
was clean-cut, confident, alert. He ought to be a good witness, but then the Committee had become a bit bored
listening to hand-picked representatives of particular
groups.

He identified himself for the record as "Chester G.
Fisher, native-born citizen, president of the Fisher Scientific Company, manufacturers, dealers, importers of laboratory supplies and scientific apparatus, Pittsburgh."

"Gentlemen," he began, "at these hearings you have

heard a great deal about 'key industries.' I am grateful to
the Committee for the opportunity to tell you something
about the master-key of all American industries, the key
to our future national progress in every industrial sphere."

This was an unusual start and the Senators sat up and
took notice. Fisher kept them at attention for more than
half an hour. Swiftly he traced the dramatic plight of this
nation, cut off from supplies of reagent chemicals, laboratory glassware, all sorts of precision instruments from microscopes to telescopes, all of which had formerly been imported from Germany. He related actual anecdotes and by
means of simple, specific examples showed the vital character of research. He told of the struggling beginnings to
manufacture laboratory equipment in this country and he
concluded with a couple of stories that illustrated what scientific research would mean in the industrial development
of this country.

"We must not be caught again," he declared, "with this
master-key to industrial progress and national defense in
the hip pocket of pants that have gone to the presser's."

Fisher's plea was ably seconded by forceful John M.
Roberts, president of the Scientific Apparatus Makers' Association, by Dr. H. N. Ott of the Spencer Lens Company,
and by the distinguished glass-maker of Vineland, New
Jersey, Colonel E. E. Kimble. Though these scientific industries were then in embryonic state, the men promised
that, if given tariff protection against the unscrupulous
competition from Germany, American research would be
independent of all imported reagents and instruments. To
the Association of University Purchasing Agents, which
opposed the protective tariff, this seemed a very rash

PLASTICS SERVE SEARCHLIGHTS.

promise. But this second World War has shown how well it has been kept.

A year ago that same Chester Fisher again sat in the witness chair in Washington, not in the ornate, Victorian committee room of the Capitol, but in one of the teeming temporary buildings, beside the desk of a War Production Board administrative official. The master-key industry for which he had so eloquently argued twenty years before had been put by the WPB in the classification of "Sports and Playground Equipment," rated, so far as priorities were concerned, as very strictly and thoroughly nonessential.

When the man who wrote those regulations was an adolescent a kindly great aunt must have sent him one of those little chemical sets that have successfully infected many budding young chemists with the itch to experiment, but in his case it could not have worked. How the tools of research and plant control could ever be lumped together with badminton rackets, trout flies, and diving-boards is incomprehensible in this day and generation, yet even after they had been properly classified, the makers of scientific instruments had to make journey after journey to Washington to educate a succession of twelve different administrators none of whom knew a test tube from a blow-pipe.

All that has been changed now, but in the early days an application for a few pounds of stainless steel to make crucible tongs for lifting the white-hot platinum and porcelain vessels out of furnaces was returned two weeks later with the query. "Cannot you use wood?"

When the rush to increase the country's output of aluminum was at a critical stage, the Aluminum Company of America was building 42 laboratories absolutely necessary to check five different steps on the production line of the light metal. The whole program was held up because it was impossible to get a few pounds of aluminum for balance arms on the fine chemical scales needed to keep the process to produce more aluminum going.

During the month of March 1942 one chemical laboratory which controls the output of one aluminum plant made 152,117 separate chemical determinations. It is reported that one chemical analysis must be made for each 160 pounds of this metal produced, so that our output of 2,000,000,000 pounds demands 12,500,000 separate laboratory determinations. To say that "We need all of the aluminum for airplanes, so none can be spared for chemical apparatus" is as illogical as to say that "We need all the wheat for flour, so none can be had for seed."

Thousands of stunning photographs of young men with good profiles in white coats holding test tubes aloft or craning their necks over shiny microscopes — laboratory calisthenics, a cynical chemist once dubbed these studied poses — have indelibly stamped the laboratory as a symbol of research, a sort of scientific Pandora's box whence emerge the chemical miracles of rayon and plastics, soapless soaps and iceless ice, or what have you. It is a shock, therefore, to find that most of the work in the laboratories is regular routine testing, analysis after analysis, essential checking of raw materials as they come into the plant, of products in process, and of finished products. The totals of such determinations in any of the modern chemically controlled industries edge up close to astronomical figures.

In one of the country's great steel plants, where much of our armor plate for ships and tanks is produced, 108,701 different analyses were made during March of this year. The average of similar reports from a number of makers of open-hearth and Bessemer steels indicates that one such determination is being made for every three tons of steel produced, or nearly 27,700,000 analyses during the year for our national output of 83,000,000 tons. Chemical control is even closer in the making of electric-furnace steel. It requires seven chemical determinations for each ton, or 35,000,000 analyses for our 5,000,000 tons of this type of high-grade steel.

If the control laboratory of an explosives plant were forced to close for half an hour, the entire plant would have to be immediately shut down. The raw materials, every batch at each stage in the manufacturing-process, and the final product must all conform to rigid specifications that must be constantly checked. U.S. Government specifications for toluene for TNT, for example, require seven different, exact determinations — for color, insoluble matter, separated water, paraffin hydrocarbons, color of the acid wash, specific gravity, and distillation range. Nitration of this toluene proceeds in three consecutive stages, and at each the nitric acid employed must be prepared to meet specific strength and composition requirements. In commercial practice the spent acid from each nitration is analyzed and fortified to bring it up again to the specific strength for the next succeeding stage. Not one of these operations can go forward until the laboratory has analyzed the acids and prescribed the correct additions to be made. In the manufacture of smokeless powder, the nitrogen content must be controlled to within 2/100 of a single per cent — .02% — for as tiny a variation as that will seriously upset ballistic calculations. To produce our stupendous output of all sorts of explosives the chemical laboratories of these munitions plants are making more than 33,000 determinations every day.

Production in every vital war industry is controlled by the constant checks of chemical analysis, not only of chemicals, explosives, combat gases, medicines, plastics, gasoline, lubricants, rubber and synthetic rubber, but also of tanks, planes, bombs, shells, rifles and guns, cartridges, shell-filling, and even ships. The Government has its own laboratories with trained staffs at all its arsenals, ordnance plants, shipyards, naval stations, submarine bases, torpedo depots, camps, and hospitals. The requirements of modern technological warfare are not only many, they are also exacting to the nth degree.

But when Chester Fisher called the laboratory the master-key to our industrial progress he was not thinking of this great, important work of chemical control. He had in mind just what the laboratory connotes to you and me, the home of research, birthplace of scientific advance and new industrial developments.

Quite recently, as Henry Wallace pointed out in his famous "cradle to the grave" speech, we have at long last achieved the means of providing a decent living for every person on this planet who knows how to do something useful. After some 5,000,000 years of toil and hunger under an economy of scarcity, the human race through a long, painful series of trials and errors has invented techniques that make possible an economy of abundance. Plenty is now practical. All of us agree that now we have the tools to reach the goal the caveman sought when he first tamed fire and cultivated his first crop with a sharpened stick.

We recognize, too, that most of this technical progress has been made within the past century, a thin, thin frosting on a very thick cake of material accomplishment. We are confident, however, that this astonishing mechanical and chemical progress is only at its beginning. This is not a fond hope, for we have perfected a wonderful new tool, research, the master-key to more and greater technical triumphs.

It is clear, if only we stop to think of it, that in the past twenty-five years we have been passing through a technical revolution that has enormously increased our ability to provide an abundance for all. Depressions, wars, all sorts of political upheavals have obscured these more fundamental, more revolutionary changes, but they have not stopped them.

It is also quite evident that the mainspring of this recent progress has been chemistry. Chemical processes and chemical products have steadily but silently extended their influence in all fields till we discover with astonishment that what we have thought of as a mechanized war is in reality waged from a chemical base.

This surprise of ours is nothing new. Even a man who does not know a nut from a bolt finds a machine more simple and comprehensible than a chemical reaction. A block and tackle is tangible and understandable. The simplest chemical process — say, common salt treated with sulphuric acid to yield Glauber's salt and hydrochloric acid — is still at its core a mystery to the wisest chemist. He knows what happens and a lot about how it happens, but nothing about why it happens. Furthermore, we all handle many machines and all sorts of mechanical devices every day while we seldom even see any chemicals — except in the drugstore — and when we do use them, we seldom think what they are. From one year's end to the other most of us never touch a single tiny lump of sulphur, yet every year each of us — men, women, and children — actually consumes on the average 12½ pounds of the yellow element. We consume it, however, in fertilizers, refined gasoline, in steel, paints, rayon, paper, textile, explosives, and indeed in almost every manufactured article.

Man learned long ago two great ways of changing natural materials more to his liking, mechanical and chemical. The caveman hacked a sharp point on a stick — a mechanical operation — and then thrust it into the fire and by charring — a chemical process — toughened it. For ages we have employed these chemical means to make materials more beautiful, more durable, more useful — to turn hides into leather, fruit juice into wine, fats into soap, sand into glass. In the past quarter-century, chemists have graduated from the making of chemicals to be used as instruments for changing and modifying natural materials to the making of new chemical materials.

That is the nub of our chemical revolution, man-made materials, and these synthetic products of chemical origin are turning old industries topsy-turvy. Without them we should have no radio, no iceless refrigerator, no planes. We have seen that without them we cannot wage modern warfare, but when we are done with this wicked perversion, we shall find that chemical products are just as essential and effective munitions in our war against want and disease. They have already created new industries. They will throw open wide doors to other, greater industrial opportunities, to more employment, to undreamed-of conveniences, to better food, more goods, sounder health.

This chemical revolution of tailor-made materials is still in its infancy, but it has been stimulated greatly by wartime necessity to expand production and to find substitutes. We have been forced willy-nilly to explore new fields. It is inevitable that important peacetime developments will result. Fortunately for the postwar world an enormous amount of work is already behind us and scores upon scores of new products are ready for the market.

Ever since man used the first tool — a handy stick, no doubt, to beat off some savage beast of prey — we have had technical progress. For ages that progress was painfully slow. Very recently it has been incredibly swift. Technical progress deliberately planned, systematically organized, and intelligently directed by research is a thing of only the past twenty-five years.

Progress of this sort is not haphazard. It is thought out in advance and yet, paradoxically, it is always a big gamble. Not one chemical research in a thousand develops a useful commercial product, and to bring it from test tube to marketplace takes seldom less than five years, often as long as fifteen. Research must be backed by what a great chemical engineer, John Teeple, years ago called "patient money," and its development in this country to a point unsurpassed in any other nation has been due to the willingness of private enterprise to gamble on long-time projects.

To foster this development of research is the best — I

almost wrote the "only" — means of assuring continued
economic progress, of providing permanent, purposeful
employment by producing usable goods, of guaranteeing
a surplus out of which to build a more abundant life. Increased production of consumable goods is the only way to
create greater wealth.

In a democracy the Government can help or it can hin-
der the pioneering research whence spring better materials and improved machines that give birth to new industries. But it cannot carry on, year after year, long-time
projects whose successful issue is highly uncertain. Tax
money is not patient money.

In these days $10,000,000 is an insignificant item in a
federal budget, but what Congress would appropriate that
sum over a period of eight years to find and perfect a new
synthetic fiber in head-on competition with our established
rayon industry and our important cotton plantations? The
violent protest of the Southern Farm Bloc when rayon
cord was demonstrated to be better than cotton duck for
fabric in truck and plane tires for the Army is the perfect
answer to that leading question. To entrust the development of new products, the creation of entirely new industries, to our Government would be to subject our elected
representatives to enormous new pressures from many
vested interests. Little in the war record of our blocs en-
courages us so to promote the pressure-group idea.

It is in their very nature that no political groups can
think further than from election day to election day. Long-
term constructive planning is not one of their fortes, and
yet to scrap the plans of their opponents is one of their
favorite campaign promises. In the face of many techni-

cal difficulties and of strong competition from other metals, it has taken twenty-five years to bring magnesium to its position as a large-tonnage, successful commercial material. For a dozen years our critically essential coal-tar chemical industry plowed back into research, construction, and development work more dollars than it took in from its sales. The sensational sulfa-drugs mark the culmination of a research that began in 1908. Similar examples might be multiplied by the hundreds, and to get continuous, consecutive programs for research and development projects it would not help "to take them out of politics" by putting them under the Civil Service. The very spirit of research is killed by bureaucracy.

Most research problems start with a theory. But as Gustavus Esselen, a distinguished consulting-chemist with a great store of practical experience in business chemistry, has pointed out, "Lurking behind the hope this theory will prove sound lies the hope (compounded of curiosity and a spirit of revolution) that it will be disproved. For then the researcher will have to start all over again in his thinking. Often this leads to an entirely original approach to the problem; and originality of conception is the basis of nearly all progress, in science as well as in art and business."

As Professor H. E. Stocher has put it, "Research teaches a man to admit that he is wrong and to be proud of the fact that he does so, rather than to try with all his energy to defend an unsound plan because he is afraid that admission of error is confession of weakness." That is not the lesson that bureaucracy teaches nor the political technique that wins elections.

We do not agree very well in what way or by whom the new tools of plenty are to be employed. Without doubt we must learn how to get the greatest good for the greatest number by the old trial-and-error methods. It is the hard way. It is a wasteful process, but in the end it eventually works. The goal before us is now plain and attainable; but amid the turmoils of these great experiments we must keep these new tools bright and sharp and we should be most careful that the master-key to material progress, research, is not mislaid.

War on the chemical front — I repeat it — will not stop when the bugles on the battlefield sound "cease firing." Whatever may happen at the peace table, and afterwards, technological progress is bound to surge forward, and in this advance chemistry will be in the van. Man-made raw materials are a fact of enormous economic and political significance. We have seen how they have completely rewritten the tactics of war. They are writing new rules for business. They have made wastepaper of all the old tenets of international relations. Raymond Moley summed it all up for us when he said recently: "Atoms and electrons, plastics and alloys are on the march and the brain that does not comprehend them will sink into the dust."

INDEX

◇◇

[i

A NOTE ON THE TYPE

The text of this book is set in Caledonia, a Linotype face designed by W. A. Dwiggins. Caledonia belongs to the family of printing types called "modern face" by printers — a term used to mark the change in style of type-letters that occurred about 1800. Caledonia is in the general neighborhood of Scotch Modern in design, but is more freely drawn than that letter.

The book was composed, printed, and bound by The Plimpton Press, Norwood, Massachusetts.